THE BILLION $ SWINDLE

Foreword by
The Hon. Harrison A. Williams, Jr.
Chairman,
United States Senate
Special Committee on Aging

THE BILLION $ SWINDLE

Frauds Against The Elderly

by Amram Ducovny

Fleet Press Corporation
New York / London

for Daniel, David and Laurie

Acknowledgments

I wish to express my profound appreciation to The American Cancer Society, The American Dental Association, Arthritis Foundation, The American Medical Association, The National Better Business Bureau, and The Special Senate Committee on Aging for their cooperation in facilitating the research for this book.

Foreword

This is a book about the vulnerability of the elderly to the blandishments of the con-man, the fraud, the scheme.

Older Americans—men and women who at about age 65 must adjust to the frequently bleak world of retirement—find that they have new needs, new problems, and new questions about budgets and expenses. Consider medicine: even with Medicare, medical costs take a large share of the retiree's budget; a study of medical expenses in 1966 for urban elderly couples revealed a $284 out-of-pocket average, including $72 for Medicare premiums.

Indeed, retirement and the aging process often bring a multitude of money problems. The later years also mean an increasing temptation to reach out for the quick cure, the miraculous medicine man, and the practitioners who promise shortcuts to health. It is not surprising that the American Medical Association can estimate that a *billion* dollars a year is spent—wasted—on frauds and quack schemes.

Most older Americans have incomes far below the "Retired Couple's Budget for a Moderate Standard of Living," as announced by the U.S. Bureau of Labor Statistics in mid-1968. Frauds perpetrated on the elderly are the cruelest kind of hoax, because older Americans have less money, less access to accurate information, and greater need for qualified medical assistance than any other group in our society.

What kinds of schemes are worked on the nation's elderly? The chapters of this book present a poignant catalogue of deception: health and nutrition "gimmicks" which don't offer any help; medical devices and techniques which not only fail to cure disease, but frequently cause additional harm, nursing home frauds; investment swindles; funeral schemes, and other equally shabby half-truths or untruths that cheat the aged. Sometimes the cost of these frauds is only a few dollars, but sometimes, the cost is tragically higher.

We can all laugh at the antics of "Silent George of Shawneetown," who sold cans of condensed milk with "rabbit labels" attached, trumpeting the milk as "rich in vitamins J, U, M and P." Perhaps we can laugh at the "health lecturers" who wandered the country promising to cure arthritis with onions and water. But can we laugh at some $315 million which will be wasted in 1969 on worthless arthritis cures? Is there any humor in the operation of a bogus hearing aid firm in Iowa who cheated blind and invalided victims out of thousands of dollars?

Can we laugh off a quack scheme which keeps one elderly person from seeking competent medical attention, until it is too late?

These are not laughing matters; similarly, the problems faced by the elderly in the changing marketplace cause widespread concern. A U.S. Postal Inspector has told of a "business opportunity" which squeezed $75,000 out of hapless "investors" in just four months; the con man was selling worthless distributorships in cultured marble. Fixed incomes are the rule for most of the elderly, and in today's booming market place, too many older Americans can't keep up with product changes, new terminology, and salesmanship pressures which, if they are confusing to the average active consumer, can be absolutely bewildering to the retiree.

As the Commissioner of the U.S. Administration on Aging told our Committee:

> Day-to-day marketing practices often are in complete contrast to those to which older consumers were once accustomed... The typical supermarket before World War II stocked approximately 1,500 separate items, but today it carries over 8,000. Ninety per cent of the prescriptions written today are for drugs that were unknown 20 years ago. Many new products used every day are highly complex so that, as it has been stated by one consumer-educator, the user is called upon to be an amateur electrician, mechanic, chemist, toxicologist, dietician and mathematician—but he is rarely furnished the information needed to perform these tasks proficiently... The consumer

often does not know precisely how much he pays for consumer credit, whether one prepared food has more nutritional value than another, whether the performance of a product will, in fact, meet his needs, or which of the package sizes is really a bargain.

In the midst of such complexity, the *honest* merchant and manufacturer have difficulty getting the essential facts to consumers. In the same atmosphere, the *dishonest* salesman or entrepreneur thrives; he can make the confusion work to his advantage.

Many other factors contribute to the susceptibility of the elderly: sheer loneliness can make an older person yearn for the sound of a human voice—even a con man's; a feeling that "time is running out" and reluctance to see a doctor after a lifetime of good health can make a person easy prey for the quack; and of course, in each of us, there is the belief that in extraordinary situations, extraordinary—even magic—men and machines will pull us through.

Fortunately, we soon may know a great deal more about human susceptibility. Seven Federal agencies are participating in a study made at the request of the Special Committee on Aging; a questionnaire will be used to interview 2,800 people about their openness to health fallacies and misrepresentations. At least 20 per cent of the people interviewed will be over 65 years of age.

The government can, and must, do several things to step up the fight against quacks and con men. First, we need more and better information about the elderly as consumers; without this data, we will be handcuffed by speculation. Additionally, we need to map out a plan of action to *protect* and *inform* the elderly, along with other consumers.

Basic steps we might take include:

1. a top-to-bottom evaluation of government information programs to measure their effectiveness

2. a search for new avenues of cooperation with private organizations and agencies

3. a comprehensive legislative review of consumer protection laws already on the books (because consumer conditions, and con games, change even as last year's laws are enacted)

4. the creation of a Federal clearing-house for information related to quackery (or a more comprehensive program, such as that proposed by New York Attorney General Louis Lefkowitz, which would involve a central source for *all* fraud-detection and control information)

5. a Federal campaign to strengthen state anti-fraud agencies (the Federal Trade Commission made a start here, with a Federal-state cooperative bureau, but more is needed).

In health, in investment counseling, in land-sales protection, the goal is the same: the maintenance of an honest market-place where the elderly—and all Americans—can trade in confidence. The buyer must have all the information he needs to make an intelligent purchase. The patient must be guaranteed that he will not be led astray by the glib hucksterism of the quack. The retired couple must be assured that their savings will be protected when they attempt to do business in the market.

Most of all, we need to shed full light on the problem. I am pleased to have this opportunity to offer some remarks at the opening of a book which does, indeed, contribute to national awareness and understanding of the problems of frauds and misrepresentation. Our task now is to use the information we are gathering—every day, in every part of the country—in an all-out campaign against the shadowy operators who live and thrive on the fringe, spurned by honest manufacturers and sellers.

Senator Harrison A. Williams, Jr.
Chairman, U.S. Senate Special Committee on Aging

Contents

THE BILLION $ SWINDLE

1 The Scope of the Problem: The Senate Investigations

In the fall of 1968, the *New York Times* reported that a United States Senate Subcommittee had been "shocked and appalled" by evidence that a reputable drug firm, in its promotional literature, had called elderly patients "crocks" and "cruds." The company's method of firing up its salesmen to push a powerful drug used in the treatment of arthritis seemed more fitting to unloading spoiled fruit than selling beneficial medicine. Its brochure proclaimed:

"It is obvious that X will work in that whole host of rheumatic crocks and cruds which every general practitioner, internist and orthopedic surgeon sees every day in his practice . . . Now every bottle of 1000 X that you sell is an extra $2.80 incentive payment. Go get it . . . Let's take the kid gloves off and start slugging it out."

Subsequently, the firm admitted that this kind of language was "most regrettable."

Tragically, the idea that the elderly are fair game for juicy financial pickings is quite a prevalent and lucrative one. Conservative estimates are that senior citizens in our nation are being taken for at least a billion dollars a year. For while an otherwise scrupulous drug firm may apologize for its over-zealous hard-sell, thousands of out-and-out quacks and frauds continue to hunt for the sick, fearful, and uninformed and are rewarded with daily bonanzas.

The Senate Committee on Aging began federal inquiry into the problem in 1963. Subsequently, its Subcommittee on Frauds and Misrepresentations Affecting the Elderly (later renamed the Subcommittee on Consumer Interests of the Elderly) held hearings in 1964, 1967, and 1968. All these sessions underscored the fact that Americans in general are today paying billions of dollars for worthless medications, ineffectual and potentially dangerous medical devices, treatments given by unqualified practitioners, food fads and useless diet supplements, and other alluring products or services that make misleading promises to cure or end pain. In addition, fraud is on the rise in Mail Order Land Sales, Health Insurance Sales, Pre-need Burial Contracts, and a host of consumer swindles.

In all these areas, the elderly are the main targets and victims of what Committee Chairman Senator Harrison Williams of New Jersey described as "the highly organized high-pressure technique of the modern-day medicine man."

In California, for example, three-quarters of the population aged 65 or over have some type of chronic condition such as cancer, arthritis, heart disease, or other incurable disability. The onslaught by medical confidence men against these unfortunates was described by a spokesman for the Attorney General of California:

"The snake-oil medicine man has exchanged his stock for food supplements and has rephrased his pitch in twentieth-century language. He has added to his stock electronic devices with dials. He can cure or prevent cancer, cardiac conditions, dermatoses, rheumatism, improper blood pressure and anemia."

Equally slick con men operate across the national scene. Asked whether fraudulent schemes are on the increase, the Chief Postal Inspector of the United States answered with a definite affirmative. He also gave reasons for the increasing difficulty in prosecuting medical-fraud cases:

"Although postal inspectors still occasionally encounter medical quackery items involving electric belts, buzzers, bell ringing, and even black-magic potions guaranteed to cure all manner of disease, today's frauds are generally more sophisticated. Promoters do not so often promise outright cures for serious diseases but offer other preparations to 'aid' in curing various conditions which the American consumer finds undesirable, such as baldness, obesity, and so forth.

"Treatments are offered by mail for every conceivable condition, including cancer, diabetes, prostate trouble, asthma, arthritis, heart diseases, and impotency, to name but a few. Such schemes continue to be a source of great concern since the victims are frequently induced to attempt self-diagnosis and treatment, meanwhile deferring proper attention."

A special assistant to the President of the United States for

Consumer Affairs told the Senators of the spiraling problem and its tragic consequences:

"The aging men and women in our society are becoming increasingly a more significant percentage of our total population. As their numbers increase, so also will the incidence of fraud and quackery increase. For these people, removed—as many of them are—from the mainstream of daily business activity, cut off from the stimulation of regular 'back fence' exchanges with neighbors, become in their loneliness evermore susceptible to the blandishments of facile hucksters.

"I receive daily in my office scores of letters from older people all over the country. The range of subject matter with which these people are concerned is broad and varied, but there has been a heavy emphasis on health frauds and quackery.

"Many of the writers have despaired long since of any redress of their grievances; they want simply to share their disappointment, their sense of loss, with someone, with anyone who will offer a bit of understanding. I am tremendously impressed with this dread of loneliness that seems to run through so many of the letters and interviews with people as I run around the country.

"Others of them, confident still that frauds and quacks will somehow be searched out and restrained, plead with the eloquence of age for the Government to take some kind of action against those who would victimize the weak and the innocent."

Other testimony contained in the over 4,000-page transcript of the Senate hearings yielded a multitude of eye-openers of fraud, cruelty and pain. As Senator Williams put it:

"It seems to me that there are losses that go far beyond the original purchase price for the phony treatment, the useless gadget, the inappropriate drug or pill. How can we measure the cost in terms of suffering, disappointment, and final despair? Do we really know how many Americans are quietly using therapy of products that give them neither cure nor the hope of cure? Can we be sure that we know the full extent of operations by questionable clinics and neighborhood practitioners?"

2

Health Quackery:
A Dictionary of Frauds

During the course of its investigations, the Senate Committee took a probing look into the many aspects of fakes and swindles in the health field. It was estimated that billions of dollars a year are spent on falsely promoted products that are worthless or dangerous.

The Federal Drug Administration has compiled a dictionary of frauds in this field which underscores the size and sweep of the problem and offers tips on how to fight it. Any elderly person contemplating a purchase or treatment in any of these areas would do well to first check the FDA's conclusions.

[24

AIR PURIFIERS

Promotion of so-called air purifiers for preventing or treating respiratory infections and other types of diseases is one of today's most prevalent health swindles. Equipment is available for effective air purification, but it is much more expensive than the small units sold by some retail dealers. The latter do not have sufficient capacity for removing dust and pollen which may aggravate allergic conditions such as hay fever, and no air purifier can truthfully be promoted for treating viral or bacterial diseases such as colds, influenza, pneumonia, tuberculosis, etc. Air treatment devices are also being sold as "negative ion generators," but it has not been established that negative ions are of any value for preventing or treating diseases.

ALCOHOLISM "TREATMENTS"

Advertised "cures" for the "liquor habit" are worthless. There are no safe or easy remedies which can be relied on to permanently overcome addiction to alcohol. Recovery depends on the individual's sincere desire to stop drinking and his willingness to accept medical and spiritual help in this effort.

ANEMIA ("TIRED BLOOD") PREPARATIONS

An inexpensive blood test by your doctor will show whether you need to take an iron medicine for "tired blood." Most people don't. Symptoms of tiredness may be due to many different causes and a layman would not be able to tell whether they are caused by iron deficiency or by some other, perhaps very serious, condition. Pernicious anemia, for example, is a fatal disease if not treated properly. Self-treatment should not be attempted. "Tired blood" remedies may also do harm by masking symptoms of disease, of which anemia is one.

Arthritis Remedies

The cost of worthless preparations and treatments for arthritis and rheumatism may be much greater than the money spent on them. Postponement of proper medical care can result in serious crippling. Early treatment by physicians can reduce the crippling effects. There are many forms of arthritis which require different kinds of treatment. Inexpensive drugs can relieve the pain to some extent, but there are no drugs, devices, or methods that can truthfully be labeled as a cure.

Cancer Treatments

Cancer can be cured with early treatment by surgery, Xray, or radiation, but there are no serums, drugs, or diets that have been proved effective in curing cancer. Many cancer victims or their families spend thousands of dollars on worthless treatments. Millions of lives could be saved with prompt treatment by effective methods. Regular medical checkups are the best protection.

Colds and Cough Remedies

There are many preparations that will relieve the "miseries" of a cold to some extent, but none can truthfully be represented as a cure. Package directions tell how to use "cold remedies" safely and effectively. It is especially important to pay attention to the warnings on labels and circulars accompanying cough and cold preparations. Some of them can be harmful if improperly used. Special instructions regarding dosage for children should be followed carefully. Particular attention should be given to label information regarding conditions which should be treated by a physician.

COLITIS TREATMENTS: LAXATIVES

Beware of any product advertised as a treatment for colitis. Self-treatment should not be attempted for this complex and often serious condition. Excessive use of laxatives is one cause of colitis; high-colonic enemas should also be avoided as ineffective and sometimes harmful. It is *not necessary* to have a daily bowel movement, but it is wise to seek medical advice about chronic constipation. Heed the directions and warnings on any laxative label. Don't fall for products that promise to "break the laxative habit." It's just another gimmick—to sell laxatives.

COSMETIC QUACKERY

Good cosmetic preparations, properly applied, can help greatly to enhance personal appearance, but "miracle" cosmetics are one of the oldest—and newest—forms of quackery. The desire for youthful attractiveness, like the desire for good health, is very strong. Many people are willing to spend a great deal of money for products that promise what they cannot perform. Beware particularly of cosmetics promoted on the basis of some new special ingredient "scientifically" found to have remarkable effects.

Beware also of institutions advertising treatments that will give you a "new complexion" by chemical "face peels." Dangerous drugs in such products have caused many serious injuries.

DENTAL PLATES AND ADHERENTS

Dental health is important to everybody but especially to older people who must adjust to new foods and change their eating habits.

Getting false teeth by mail order that will fit properly is

practically impossible. Use of poorly fitting dentures is unsafe. Stabilizers and reliners can be used for temporary basing, but not as a permanent correction. See your local dentist for correctly designed dentures and for refitting when your mouth changes. Don't expect too much from powders or liquids advertised to make dentures stick better, or to cure sore gums.

DIABETES TREATMENTS

Do not use any self-diagnosis treatment, drug, or dietary food product that is not recommended by your physician. Death can result from not heeding this warning. Persons with diabetes should be under the care of a physician for regular examinations and any needed adjustment of their treatment. Beware of the advice given by "health food" promoters, vitamin salesmen, and popular diet books.

DIAGNOSTIC MACHINES

One of the biggest and most dangerous health swindles is the mechanical or electrical gadget that is supposed to tell what disease a person has and how to treat it. Thousands of such machines have been manufactured and are in use by various kinds of health practitioners to diagnose and treat every kind of human ailment.

Of course, there are legitimate medical devices such as the apparatus to determine blood pressure or the electrocardiograph used to record the action of the heart. But beware of the practitioner who has a machine supposedly capable of diagnosing or treating different kinds of diseases simply by turning dials and applying electrical contacts to the body. Such devices are fakes! Persons who suspect they are being victimized through the use of devices should communicate with the nearest office of the Food and Drug Administration.

"DOORBELL DOCTORS"

You don't hire a day laborer to fix your TV set, but many people will accept health advice from door-to-door vitamin peddlers. Especially beware of the professional-sounding person who is a walking encyclopedia on matters of diet and health. And don't fall for the "folksy" type of salesman who takes such a friendly interest in all your health problems. They are only interested in selling something.

See your doctor if you don't feel up to par and think you may need vitamins. You may have some serious condition. Don't take a vitamin or so-called help-health preparation instead of seeing your doctor. Delay may cost you more than money— you may lose your life.

EYEGLASSES BY MAIL ORDER

There are legitimate firms that fill prescriptions for eyeglasses by mail, but eyeglasses cannot be adequately or safely *fitted* by mail nor can a mail-order course in eye treatment be truthfully offered to correct defects of vision. The human eye is complex and delicate and should not be tampered with by the unskilled. An examination by a professionally trained person is necessary to fit eyeglasses correctly.

GERIATRIC FOODS

There is a growing market for foods to meet the dietary needs of older people. Some of these geriatric foods, and this includes those marketed as infant and baby foods, fill an important need. So far as nutritional factors are concerned, however, the needs of older persons are much like those of any other age group. One should not be impressed by sales pitches which represent that older people have special requirements for vitamins, minerals, proteins, etc., that are not available in inexpensive everyday food sources.

HAIR RESTORERS

Hair dyes on the market today are not harmful to the majority of people when properly used, but are dangerous when misused. Be sure to follow the directions exactly and make all prescribed skin tests to determine if you are allergic to the dye. Best results are obtained by a skilled professional operator. There is no product that will "restore" the natural color to gray hair or permanently dye the hair. Vitamin E is worthless for this purpose.

HEALTH FOODS

There are many "special dietary foods" which are valuable for people who have certain diseases. Good examples are the "low sodium" foods prescribed for heart patients and the special foods for diabetics. These must not be confused with "health foods" promoted by food faddists as dietary cure-alls.

A substitute does not exist for good food as a basis for good health. Yet today many people try to doctor themselves with so-called health foods, and such products are quite often promoted in much the same fashion as old-time patent medicines. Even the term "health food" is misleading because it implies that the products have special health-giving properties when they merely have nutritional qualities that are found in other common food products. Yoghurt has much the same nutritional value as milk; the "minerals" in black-strap molasses are mainly impurities that get in from the sugar-refining process; the iodine in kelp tablets or sea salt is adequately supplied by sea foods and iodized salt. It is not true that the American food supply is nutritionally deficient or that everybody is suffering from some kind of vitamin deficiency and therefore needs to take a food supplement.

Relying on "health foods" to keep you well can be dangerous as well as expensive. They are not better than regular foods or a substitute for regular medical checkups. Unusual foods or diets may actually be harmful in many cases.

HEALTH BOOKS

There are many books that advise the reader as to how he can enjoy better health. Unfortunately, those that become popular can rarely be considered reliable sources of health information. Many are medical nonsense—for example, a recent best-seller that advocates cod-liver oil and orange juice as a sure cure for arthritis, or another that promoted honey and vinegar as a cure-all combination for every kind of ailment. Dozens of diet books advocate practices which may be harmful to persons who take them seriously. There is no "doctor book" that can substitute for a doctor.

HEARING AIDS

Be careful in regard to advertised deafness cures and hearing aids. Before investing—investigate. Consult a qualified hearing specialist (otologist) about your hearing problems.

HEMORRHOID (PILE) TREATMENT

Mild ointments can be used to relieve soreness, itching, or burning, but will not "shrink" or cure hemorrhoids. Bleeding may indicate a serious condition calling for prompt medical treatment.

High Blood Pressure Treatments

High and low blood pressure are not diseases but may be symptoms of various diseases. There are drugs that a doctor may prescribe for such conditions but none that may legally be sold for self-medication. Contrary to a rather common idea, garlic is not good for high blood pressure. Nor have safflower-oil capsules been shown to be preventive for high blood pressure, heart diseases, or strokes. So-called health foods are often falsely claimed to be good for high (or low) blood pressure.

Hormones

The danger from self-medication with hormone drugs is so great that they may be sold only by prescription. These are potent drugs. Do not pressure your doctor to prescribe them. He will be able to decide on the basis of a thorough examination.

Impotency (Lost Manhood) Cures

Among the oldest and commonest of all health hoaxes is the Fountain of Youth type of product. A recent example is the "royal (bee) jelly" fad. Sexual rejuvenation is constantly promised or implied by fringe promoters of foods, drugs, devices, and cosmetics. The fact is that such claims have no scientific foundation. Sexual vitality continues until late in life for many individuals, but there is no form of self-medication that will insure this.

Kidney Remedies

There is no known preparation that can legally be labeled for self-medication as a cure or treatment for "kidney trouble," or diseases of the kidney or bladder. These are serious ailments, not to be treated by do-it-yourself methods.

MAIL-ORDER MEDICINES

Despite the efforts of the Post Office Department and the Food and Drug Administration, health swindles continue to be the leading category of mail fraud. Be very suspicious of drugs and health devices that are promoted by mail with claims for treatment or prevention of disease. Such promotions nearly always contain some element of quackery.

POLYUNSATURATES

No sound scientific basis exists for the current diet fad theory that hardening of the arteries or strokes can be prevented simply by adding unsaturated fats to the otherwise unchanged ordinary diet. TV advertising for food products is not a good source of medical advice on such matters. Popular diet books advocating the theory are equally unreliable and have been debunked by recognized authorities.

PSORIASIS TREATMENTS

Several drugs have long been used in preparations that temporarily relieve this troublesome skin condition. The underlying cause of psoriasis is unknown, however; no drugs have any permanent effect on it.

PYORRHEA CURES

Soreness and bleeding of the gums may be signs of many different diseases. See your dentist or physician. There is no drug product that can truthfully be promoted for self-treatment of these conditions.

REDUCING PRODUCTS

"Fooling the fat" is the golden opportunity of an army of get-rich-quick promoters. Their theme song is "get slim quick" by means of drugs, gadgets, and diet plans of every description. Pseudo-scientific diet books become national best-sellers because so many people want to believe that they can eat as they please and still take off weight. Overeating is the basic cause of overweight. Careful and proper dieting is the treament. Calories DO count in weight control. One's physical condition must be considered in relation to any drastic diet program and this calls for the advice of a physician.

RHEUMATISM RELIEVERS

Aches and pains in the joints, nerves, and muscles are apt to be referred to by the public as rheumatism. There are many causes. Simple pain relievers for temporary use, such as aspirin, are the only means of self-treatment. A doctor should be consulted regarding any persistent pain.

RUPTURE DEVICES (TRUSSES)

Surgery is usually necessary for successful treatment. No truss or other self-treatment can truthfully be promoted as a cure or to permit unlimited activity. Use of a truss, except as directed by a physician, may delay or complicate proper treatment.

SEA WATER (MINERALS)

A frequently revived health swindle is the sale of bottled

ocean water or sea salt with the claim that it supplies minerals that are essential to life. This is as phony as the legendary "goldbrick" or the deed to the Brooklyn Bridge. Foods we eat every day contain all necessary minerals in much greater abundance than ocean water.

SINUS PAIN RELIEVERS
Aspirin and other pain relievers may afford temporary relief, but cure requires medical attention.

ULCER CURES
Antacid preparations may help to relieve pain from stomach ulcers caused by hyperacidity, but anyone suffering from an ulcer should be under the care of a physician. Early symptoms of stomach cancer may resemble those of stomach ulcer. There are no drugs that can legally be sold for treatment of ulcers without a prescription.

VIBRATOR (MASSAGE) DEVICES
A great variety of vibrator devices have been put on the market. These differ widely in outward appearances, but they are generally alike mechanically—they have an electric motor with an off-center drive shaft.

Vibrators are essentially for massage, which is often useful for temporary relief of muscular stiffness, aches, and pains. Contrary to promoters' claims, vibrators are not effective for curing diseases such as arthritis, rheumatism, nervous disorders, heart conditions, and the like. Nor are vibrators effective for "spot" reducing or for reducing body weight.

VITAMINS—FALSE CLAIMS

The American food supply is the best in the world. Daily use of common foods such as vegetables, fruits, milk, eggs, meat, fish, and whole grain or enriched bread and cereals will supply all nutritional needs. Yet millions of persons are wasting money on special foods and on vitamins and mineral mixtures.

High-pressure selling frightens people into the false belief that almost everyone is suffering from, or is in danger of, one or more vitamin deficiencies. Diet-book writers, lecturers, and an army of vitamin sales agents are busy promoting this false theory. Expensive vitamin products are easy to sell when recommended as fountains of youth and general cure-alls for every kind of disease. This is especially dangerous if ailing people are led to put off proper medical attention.

Beware of the door-to-door vitamin agent who claims more than is stated on the label of his product. Some vitamins are harmful if you take too much for too long. It is not true that any significant group in our population needs additional vitamins. By patronizing a modern food store, you can easily supply all nutritional needs. If you don't feel well, tell your doctor what you are eating before you pay big money for vitamins. He can advise you whether you need them.

WRINKLE REMOVERS

There are no creams, lotions, masks, or plasters that will prevent, correct, or remove wrinkles.

3 | Arthritis: Profit in Pain

One of the most lucrative of the health frauds are "cures" and "treatments" for arthritis—with an average annual take of about $300,000,000.

Anyone or anything claiming to cure arthritis is a phony. Some forms of arthritis can be partially helped, the disease may go into spontaneous remission, pain may be lessened by drugs, but the disease is presently incurable.

Although arthritis does not necessarily strike the elderly, it is a chronic disease that rarely proves fatal and therefore is an affliction which carries into old age. Of the approximately thirteen million arthritics in the United States, some nine million are past the age of 45.

Thus, the symptoms and the extreme pain of the disease merge with the symptoms of aging and intensify the suffering from a disease which is by itself difficult enough to cope with.

According to a 1962 survey conducted by the Arthritis Foundation, arthritics annually spend some $435,000,000 on proprietary products and treatments. Jerry J. Walsh, Educational Consultant to the Foundation, estimates that $315,000,000 of this total is spent on worthless remedies—nostrums, odd-ball diets, weird devices, fallacious books, and useless clinic treatments.

Walsh, himself an arthritic, admits that before he got wise, he spent about $3,500 on phony treatments. He now tours the country alerting arthritics to the newest wrinkles in the quack con game. Yet for all his knowledge, Walsh recognizes that the pain of the disease and its debilitation is of an intensity that can blot out rational behavior.

After telling the Senate Committee on Aging of the scores of quack cures he has exposed, he was asked by a member: "If somebody brought you a new 'medicine' and said it would relieve your pain, what would you do?"

Walsh was forthright: "To be honest, Senator, if nobody was looking, I'd give it a try."

Walsh was hardly surprised when, in a three-week period following his testimony, he received 4,137 letters from arthritis sufferers recommending 231 products ranging in price from $2 to more than $200—including many "cures" or "lasting remedies."

The Foundation's figures and Walsh's exposures are seconded by the Food and Drug Administration, which has traditionally considered arthritis-product misrepresentation the most wide-spread drug-quackery problem. Over the years it has taken action against hundreds of promoters. However, as diligent as have been its labors, it is still no match for the merchants who promise respite or cure to the pain-wracked sufferers.

A severely crippled elderly woman told the Senators of her experiences, which were almost a text of quack cures. Among the treatments recommended to her: alfalfa tea and the plunging of hands into hot and cold water; sun lamps; "one woman told me that she gets a successful treatment by calling Dr. F. on the phone;" salves and a box containing "numerous little bottles with lavender caps" over which a little transparent crystal ball was swung.

A director of an arthritis clinic told the Committee why the task of protecting the elderly arthritic is a most difficult one:

"In a study of 100 patients (60 over the age of 45), 60 per cent continued to try such remedies as alfalfa seed, liniments, cod-liver oil, sea brine, etc., even while under treatment.

"The patients did not mention these experiments to the attending physician because they said they had not been asked directly by the doctor.

"Twenty-eight per cent reported incidents prior to treatment at the clinic in which they felt physicians were in too big a hurry, did not know anything about arthritis, or said there was nothing that could be done about it.

"These attitudes need to be changed, and the responsibility of the physician in changing them is paramount."

There are two main categories of misrepresented remedies: those that may even give temporary relief but make claims far beyond the true value, and those that are either worthless or harmful and issue claims that are outright lies.

Take the case of Dr. Robert E. Liefman, inventor of the drug

Liefcort, which supposedly cures arthritis by restoring the balance of body hormones.

Liefman, who practices in Montreal, Canada, received world-wide attention in 1962 when *Look* magazine reported his theories. That same year, both Canadian and United States authorities banned the distribution or retail sale of Liefcort. However, as a licensed doctor, he still pursues his legal right to prescribe it to his own patients. And despite warnings by the American Medical Association, the Arthritis Foundation, the FDA, and Canadian authorities, patients keep on coming.

Liefman claims to have "cured" 7,000 patients. No mention of failures.

The "cure" is quite easy to come by. One perfectly healthy investigator visited the Liefman clinic and waited while long lines of patients paraded through. He finally got to see a nurse, whom he told that he was suffering from arthritis in his arm. She took his blood pressure and for $10 he received a bottle of the secret formula.

Another investigator did the whole thing by mail—*sans* examination—and ended up with the same bottle of brown liquid.

Since the drug is banned in the United States, it must be smuggled across the border. A former secretary-receptionist at the Montreal clinic told a Canadian newspaperman: "The packages for the United States didn't go through the mail. I prepared them separately and another employee took them to the United States."

Liefman-type clinics have existed in Bronxville, New York, and Greenwich, Connecticut. Liefman's Montreal clinic does a land-office business with patients flying in from every section of the United States.

That Liefman himself will ever visit the United States is doubtful. There is a warrant out for his arrest in this country. The charge: peddling a female sex hormone as a cure for baldness.

Mexican physicians and clinics with arthritis cures are also plentiful. One drug, sold in Mexico and brought back to the United States by arthritics for injection by their own physicians, was found to be worthless in the treatment of the disease, but capable of causing a serious blood ailment. Two known deaths have resulted from treatment with this drug.

But elderly arthritics need not wander to foreign lands to find slag at the end of the rainbow. The cure merchants are industriously seeking them.

The American Medical Association states categorically: "Nothing a person eats or doesn't eat will cause or cure arthritis." Yet a number of recent best-selling books have promoted worthless diets for arthritics.

One non-medical author—who listed a string of fictitious academic degrees—claimed relief could be obtained through a complicated diet, the mainstays of which were cod-liver oil and orange juice. After hearings before the Federal Trade Commission, these claims were ordered halted.

Another widely distributed book took up the cudgels for honey and vinegar as a treatment for arthritis and other diseases. The federal government promptly took court action against misrepresentation for a honey-and-vinegar product promoted through the book.

The products and devices offered the arthritic by quacks are as varied as they are worthless. Two of the all-time champion products—and still going strong—are "Sea Water" and "Immune Milk."

"SEA WATER"—which is condensed to about ten times its normal concentration of minerals—goes for about three dollars a pint. Despite seizure of bottles of the stuff by federal authorities and the FDA Commissioner's warning of "a nationwide sea-water swindle," it is still being hawked with testimonials praising "this miracle of nature for its relief-giving rejuvenation of pain-ridden bodies."

"IMMUNE MILK" supposedly gets its power to conquer arthritis from antibodies produced in the udders of cows injected with certain vaccines. A quart costs about $1.70. Plain milk, at one fifth the price, is equally worthless in treating arthritis but much more nutritious.

Other fraudulent nostrums include:

THE GLORIFIED ASPIRIN: According to drug law-enforcement officials, the analgesic type of product known as "the glorified aspirin" is probably the greatest seller among arthritis products. Hundreds of these high-priced pills—whose only active ingredient is aspirin—are being offered today. Arthritis sufferers are spending millions of dollars on these elaborate concoctions—backed by equally elaborate and high pressure promotions—when they could get the same result from plain aspirin at but a fraction of the cost.

INTERNAL MEDICATIONS: Through the years scores of internal medications have been touted as cures or treatments for arthritis. Number one in this category is Tri-Wonda. The come-on for Tri-Wonda was an ad which read: "Arthritis? I have been wonderfully blessed in being able to return to active life after suffering from head to foot with muscular soreness and pain. Most all joints seemed affected. According to medical diagnosis, I had Rheumatoid Arthritis, Rheumatism, and Bursitis. For free information write ——— ."

Those who did write were deluged with literature claiming "amazing" relief from a three-bottle remedy consisting of vitamins, minerals, herbs, and laxative preparations. The product, which cost the buyer $12.50, is completely worthless, yet it took the FDA almost a decade of legal battles to obtain a ruling which bars the promotion and interstate sale of Tri-Wonda.

Products similar to Tri-Wonda—or variations of the theme—are on the market today. The FDA has legislation on the books to deal with them, but has not the funds or the staff to enforce the laws. As the FDA Commissioner put it: "We can only handle so many at one time because you generally have an expensive investigation and you have quite often a prolonged and expensive litigation."

Copper bracelets are perhaps the oldest "folk medicine" remedy for relief of the pain of arthritis. This myth persists with the tenacity of superstition. A medical expert on arthritis vividly brought this home in testimony before the Senate Committee on Aging:

"When I was a boy, back around 1894, my mother was suffering from arthritis, and she got one of these contrivances which is attached to the wrist... It is similar in some ways to the copper bands you have seen your friends who have arthritis wearing around their wrists. In fact, I saw such a band not very long ago on a very distinguished doctor and professor in New York City who suffered from arthritis. I was surprised to see this gentleman, who was a great expert on the diseases of the lungs, had resorted in desperation to this very rudimentary, so-called cure for arthritis."

The Arthritis Foundation is not surprised. It knows that sales of these useless devices are booming among those driven to desperation.

The arthritic has his choice of innumerable worthless mechanical contraptions which promoters promise will relieve their misery. These devices outsell drugs by at least two to one, with sun and heat lamps, heating pads, and vibration machines in most frequent use. The Arthritis Foundation estimates that 14 per cent of all arthritics use some type of vibrating machine. This, despite a federal government ruling that it is illegal to offer vibrators for the relief of arthritis and rheumatism.

Other more bizarre creations would fit comfortably into the Rube Goldberg category, yet they sell.

Promoters are up-to-date. A decade ago magnetism and magnetic belts were in vogue. Today, "radiation" and uranium are the key words. It took scientists eons to split the atom, but it took con men no time at all to cash in with the Zonet Applicator, which through its "Z-Ray" expanded all the atoms of the body to produce perfect health. Price: $50.

Then there was the Oxydonor, a metal disk clipped to the ankle and then immersed in cold water. The promoters promised that this gadget would "reverse the death process into life process" and cure arthritis.

Colored lights have also had their day in the quack-cure field. These did nothing more than beam spectra of light on the sufferer.

Not all the devices are worthless—some are even dangerous. The Inducto-Scope, for example, was supposed to cure arthritis through "magnetic induction" when rings were placed over the afflicted area and an attached plug inserted into a wall socket. The process exposed the arthritic to severe electric shock.

Current best-selling devices are the various "uranium" treatments. One gadget is the "Wonder Glove," a mitten selling for $100 that allegedly was lined with uranium ore. Or there is the Cosmos Radioactive Pad which is placed wherever its "emanation" will do the most good. "Radiations from uranium" as treatment have been offered to people who will come and sit in tunnels and mines. For fifteen years arthritics have flocked to the Free Enterprise Mine in Boulder, Montana, a worked-out uranium mine, where, for $3 per treatment they sat in automobile seats in the mine shaft 85 feet underground. In 1967, about 2,500 people from all over the United States sat for an average of approximately fifteen "treatments" each.

For all the various radiation cures the FDA has one word: useless! It also adds this caution: "Any product emitting radioactivity to affect functions of the body is dangerous to use without medical supervision."

In addition to these devices there are the phony spas and "arthritic" clinics. One such clinic claims to have treated more than 10,000 patients in a five-year period. Undoubtedly the majority of these were elderly.

Treatments at the clinics are varied. Most popular is hydrotherapy, colonic irrigation, chiropractic adjustment, Swedish massage—including salt rubs, use of devices and vitamin injections.

Their promotional operations run like this:

Newspaper and magazine advertisements invariably urge the reader to send for a FREE BOOKLET. A request brings not only an elaborate, usually large brochure detailing the facilities, care, and presumed benefits available, but a flood of follow-up correspondence. If the recipient does not respond to the original brochure, scare letters are soon received, pointing out the folly of delaying an appointment and the chance for new life and new hope. Another frequent procedure is to send a "personal case history" form for the patient to fill out and return, so that the "professional" staff can make recommendations regarding the case. One clinic goes so far as to call its form a Personal Diagnostic Evaluation sheet. This in effect is diagnosis by mail.

Once an arthritis victim has responded to the advertising of such clinics, he may even be subjected to solicitation from promoters of other questionable health schemes. Evidence strongly suggests an exchange of mailing lists.

The promotional material from all "arthritis" clinics is marked by striking similarities. Typically, each clinic claims that (1) a thorough physical examination is needed and will be given, (2) treatment methods are based on their own research, observations and experience, (3) the treatment is "different" and not to be found elsewhere, (4) the entire body is treated not just the arthritis and rheumatism which are caused by other disorders, (5) their staffs know the many causes of arthritis and rheumatism and are able to remove them, and (6) arthritis and rheumatism are successfully treated and major benefits, even cure, can be expected by almost every patient.

The generously illustrated brochures are undoubtedly appealing to arthritics. The repeated references to "professional" staff and "professional" methods can sound authoritative to the layman and make the optimistic claims seem believable.

However, there is strong evidence that in practice the clinics are far less than professional. The diagnostic techniques used are not able to determine accurately whether the symptoms are of a rheumatic disease. As a result, many patients who do not have arthritis or rheumatism can be so diagnosed and treated.

Claims by nearly every clinic that its particular treatment program for the rheumatic diseases is "different" certainly are true. When compared with modern methods used by physicians specializing in arthritis, the treatments offered by the clinics, and their concepts of rheumatic diseases, are in direct conflict with authoritative medical opinion based on years of controlled, scientific research and clinical observation.

Here are a few "clinic" staples:

Electrotherapy, a very vague term, presumably refers to forms of diathermy, a means of providing deep heat. Such treatment methods are very widely used to give some relief of pain and discomfort, but cannot be said to affect the cause or course of the disease. Bathing facilities, such as steam, Finnish or sitz baths, although offering temporary relief of minor aches and pains, certainly have no effect on the disease process.

Colon therapy, given much prominence by the clinics, was generally discarded as ineffectual at least thirty to forty years ago in treating the rheumatic diseases. It may also be harmful through disruption of normal function.

Chiropractic adjustments are prescribed to relieve supposed pressure on the nerves caused by a possible slight misalignment of the vertebrae, and thus restore balanced function to the nervous system and normalize digestion and assimilation of food. According to the AMA, ignorance of human physiology and pathology is manifest in this fundamental chiropractic concept which has no place in the modern approach to arthritis and rheumatism. In addition, such adjustments can cause great havoc to an arthritic spine.

"Plasmatic therapy" is described in meaningless terminology as an "original method of introducing heat into the circulatory system, causing stimulation of the blood cells." "Vitamin efficiency" appears to be an all-inclusive phrase: "whenever vitamin or mineral deficiency is evidenced, the body is brought up to par with the needed vitamins, mineral or hormone." Repeated studies have failed to show that lack or excess of any vitamin, mineral or specific hormone is involved in the course of, or is of value in, the treatment of the rheumatic diseases.

The clinics' concepts regarding diet seem to be based on the tenets of nutrition faddism rather than scientific knowledge. A commonly expressed need to "alkalinize" the body is, in fact, not only exceedingly difficult to accomplish but is incompatible with health.

The few clinics that have medical doctors among their staffs and use some drugs in their treatments mention these facts with an air of apology: "However, drugs are not used in an attempt to correct disease. Their use is restricted to the relief of symptoms until the regular treatments have time to control the situation."

Testimonials are part of all their promotional literature:

"Ninety-six per cent of our patients enthusiastically praise the benefits they enjoy from our treatments..." "Happy results in the many cases treated..." "...our specialized and correlated treatments are essential in also correcting 'hopeless' conditions..." "Be restored to health." "PERMANENT RELIEF."

Without mentioning the word "cure," cure is implied by the use of such statements. And cure is implicit in the repeated claims that they are able to eliminate the causes of arthritis, thus enabling the body to regain its normal functions.

Here is a testimonal the "arthritis clinics" will never use. It was read to a Senate Committee on Frauds and Misrepresentations Affecting the Elderly because the witness was hospitalized and unable to appear in person.

"When the doctor told me I had arthritis, I cried. My sister had it after her third child was born, and though it cleared up after six months of gold-injection treatment, she had terrible pain. I was afraid because gold did not work for me and Cortisone only helped some.

"At that time nobody told me about exercises and splints or heat to keep my joints straight. Sometimes I thought my arthritis would just go away. I'd have as long as a week when I could walk across the room as though there was nothing wrong with me, then my hands and feet and knees would swell and hurt so that I couldn't get up to try to walk.

"I got pretty discouraged, so I went to this chiropractor who said he could get me well, but it would take a long time. He worked on my spine and he told me to cut down the Cortisone. I did, but at the end of the year I was worse than ever.

"He said it was the fault of the Cortisone.

"I was very depressed when I read an ad for the Ball Clinic which said they had helped thousands. I wrote and asked them for references and got the names of three people I could write to. The answers I got from these people said they had gotten good results, so my husband and I borrowed the money and I went out for a six-week period, which is what the Ball Clinic said I'd need.

"It turned out to cost twice as much as they said it would.

"The first thing they did was to make me come off the Cortisone altogether, then they gave me spinal manipulations, colonic irrigations, radio wave, ultrasound treatments, massages and baths, and put me on a no-meat diet. I managed to walk into the clinic but at the end of six weeks I was so sick and in such pain I could not leave. They told me I must stay for two more weeks, but even then they had to carry me out on a stretcher. Those last two weeks cost $400. All together my stay cost almost $900. It took us a long time to pay back the money we had borrowed.

"Up to about three months ago I still got letters from the Ball Clinic urging me to go back; they also wrote that if I could get three other arthritics to go they would send me a check for $5, or they would give me a lower rate when I came back.... Eventually I went to the arthritis clinic at Seton Hall College of Medicine in Jersey City.

"Right now I still can't walk, but I have had an operation on one hip and I only hope that everything will turn out all right.

"I would not want to tell anybody with arthritis what to do, but I feel if I had been able to find out what I now know early enough I'd never have gotten so bad.... Treatment is a steady and, I have to admit, a sometimes depressing struggle, but I wish I had back the two and a half years I spent trying other things or just giving up."

Of all the quacks and charlatans operating in the medical field, the arthritis con merchant seems to be the most *au courant,* the most imaginative in his methods. Undoubtedly, a few days after man makes a lunar landing, moon rays, earth or "honey and vinegar" from the moon will be offered to arthritis sufferers. And they will be bought because of the pain and nature of the disease. As one elderly woman, who had been duped many times, told the Senate Committee: "If we fall for the phony, and sooner or later most of us do, it is because nobody knows why it comes or how and when it goes."

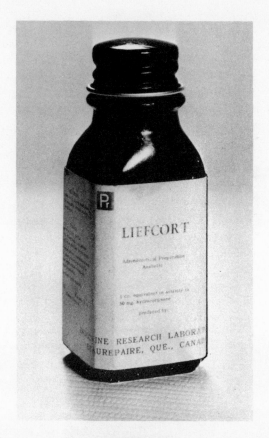

LIEFCORT

The pain suffered by arthritis victims is sometimes so great that they seek out cures and medication officially denounced and prosecuted by the Arthritis Foundation, the American Medical Association, the Federal Drug Administration, and physicians. Such was the case with Liefcort, manufactured in Canada. American victims travelled there to purchase this worthless "remedy" condemned by the U. S. and Canadian governments. Dr. Liefmann faces prosecution if and when he comes to the United States.

Promotion for "Honegar" cure. Sale of this cure-all was prohibited for making false claims.

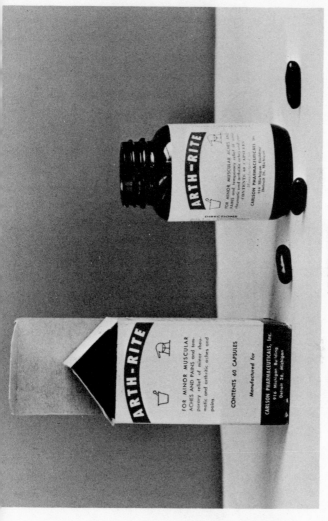

ARTH-RITE

A compound of alfalfa and vitamins. It was found to be of no benefit in the treatment of arthritis and rheumatism. These glorified aspirins sell for $5.95.

TRI-WONDA

It took the federal government nine years of prosecution to get this three-bottle fraudulent "cure" for arthritis banned from interstate distribution. Cost: $10.

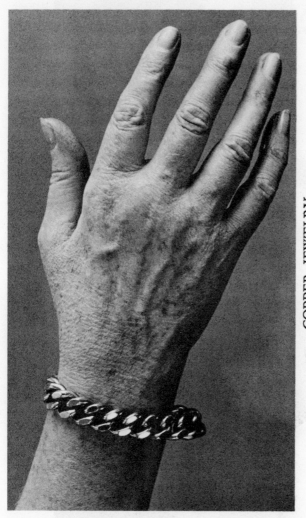

COPPER JEWELRY

Copper bracelets are just one of the many metal jewelry items foisted on arthritics by deceitful promotors. Wearing one on each wrist to set up a so-called "curative Circuit" is claimed to obtain greatest benefits. Price $2.50 to $19.95.

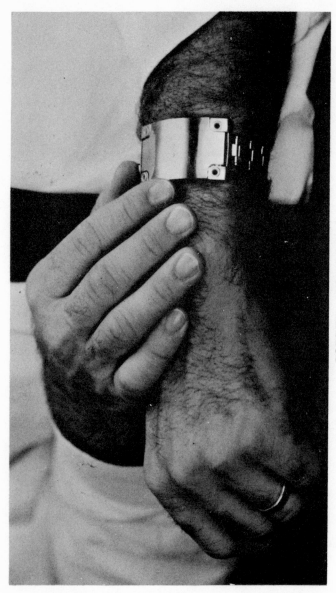

COPPER JEWELRY

One of the more elegant of the copper bracelet frauds, the Electro-Galvanic Bracelet claimed to relieve the wearer of arthritis pain.

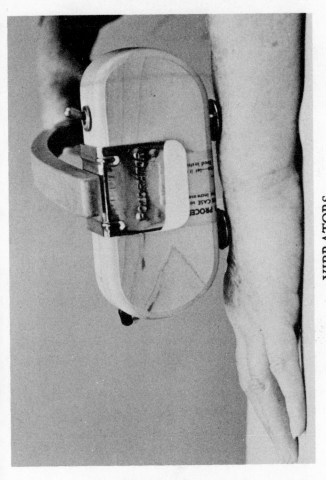

VIBRATORS

Vibrators can actually cause severe damage to victims of arthritis. Although they can relax muscular tension, they cure nothing and can be very dangerous.

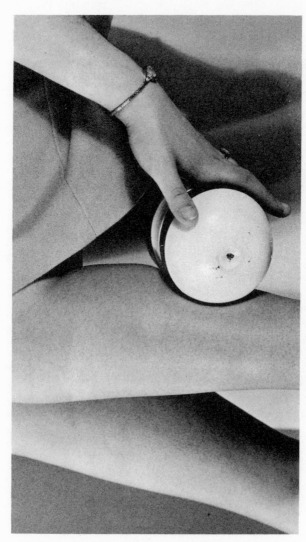

FERGUSON'S ZERRET APPLICATOR

This plastic device contains "Zerret Water" alleged to produce "Z-rays", unheard of in science. The real contents was tap water, for which victims paid up to $50; the promoters were jailed.

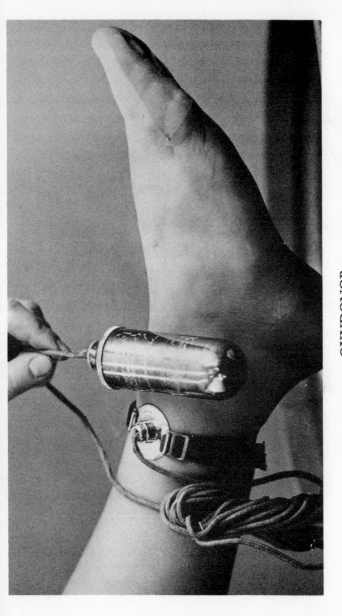

OXYDONOR

This gadget was claimed to "reverse the death process into the life process" and cure arthritis and rheumatism. Price: $30.

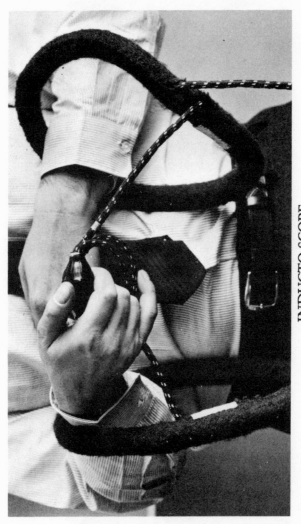

INDUCTO-SCOPE

This device (seized by the FDA) claimed to cure arthritis through "magnetic induction" by placing the rings over the afflicted areas and inserting the plug into a wall socket. Its only achievement was to expose the sufferer to the further hazard of electric shock.

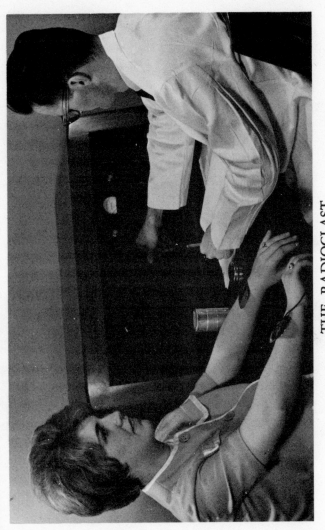

THE RADIOCLAST

This was offered for the diagnosis and treatment of brain diseases and diseases of the spinal cord, lungs, heart, and eyes. It was condemned by court order in 1959.

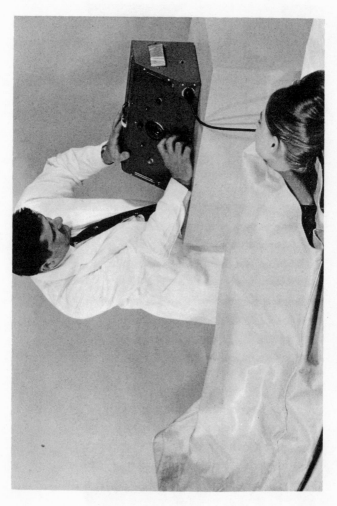

PLASMATIC THERAPY INSTRUMENT

The inventor claimed this device "directly heats the blood." The inventor claimed to have sold more than 1,000 of these devices.

4

Nutritional Quackery:
From Snake Oil to Safflower Oil

Because Americans are probably the most health-conscious people in the world, nutritional quackery has become one of the smoothest and best-organized rackets in the country. Five hundred million dollars is the take from the gullible, according to the American Medical Association.

Persons of advancing years are naturally preoccupied with prolonging their lives and keeping their health and are particularly susceptible to food frauds. Also, elderly people usually have time to spare and time to read. The health hucksters are aware of this and the market is glutted with literature containing "expert" advice about food, all of which boils down to nutritional nonsense.

All authoritative reports on the nutritional requirements of older people indicate no appreciable difference from that of younger adults. However, according to the food con men, all elderly people need a variety of food supplements at all times and in all seasons. The aged are led to believe that the afflictions of old age are dietary in origin and the promoter has the right capsule, vitamin, or food to make them feel young again.

Testifying before the Senate Committee on Frauds and Misrepresentations Affecting the Elderly, a nutritional expert gave the following examples of food-scare techniques in books or ads and branded them all as "flagrant lies or gross misrepresentations":

(1) The alarming fact is that food—fruits and vegetables and grains—now being raised on millions of acres of land that no longer contains minerals, are starving us—no matter how much of them we eat.

(2) Heart disease, high blood pressure, diabetes, atherosclerosis, and cancer have increased tremendously since grain was first milled and vitamin E and all of the B vitamins discarded in the milling process.

(3) If you fear that your reflexes are slowing down and you are unable to make those split-second decisions behind your steering wheel, now is the best time for you to start taking thiamine tablets. Thiamine is the best builder of mental alertness and is essential in the diet of an alert, careful automobile driver.

(4) The fifteen or more B vitamins are so meagerly supplied in our American diet that almost every person lacks them.

(5) Even if you eat lots of protein foods, you may be

deficient in several amino acids with resulting fatigue and depression, vague aches and pains. Buy ——— .

(6) Almost 80 per cent of Americans are starving in the midst of plenty... the result is lack of strength and energy, frequent illness, and infections and onslaught of premature aging. Buy ——— .

(7) Adding enzymes to the diet is especially important to the middle-aged and elderly since the secretion of natural gastric juices often decline as we grow older... If you feel you are "getting old" you certainly owe it to yourself to try adding extra enzymes to your diet. Buy ——— .

(8) When the daily intake of Lecithin is not great enough to satisfy the demands... many undesirable reactions may occur. These reactions may be similar to vitamin deficiencies such as nervousness, fatigue, emotional instability, headaches, insomnia, and many other symptoms. Supplement your diet with a rich source of natural Lecithin with ——— .

(9) Nutritional deficiencies are apt to increase with age and are a primary source of the afflictions of old age. Why take chances with your health? Try ——— vitamins.

All these statements are calculated to push the elderly into buying a supermarket full of food and vitamin supplements.

And what do they get? If they are lucky, a harmless concoction such as a protein supplement worth 19 cents a day if taken in the prescribed dose and whose nutritional value is equal to half a cent's worth of skimmed, dried milk. Or any one of the many vitamin E tablets which sell quite well despite the fact that nutritional authorities have yet to find a documented case of vitamin E deficiency in a human being.

If they are unlucky, they will believe the claims of "cure-all" items and delay proper and prompt treatment of their ailments.

Perhaps the foremost of these cruel hoaxes was a best-seller called Nutri-Bio.

George P. Larrick, former FDA Commissioner told the Senate Committee on Aging the Nutri-Bio story:

"Investigation disclosed that Nutri-Bio was being promoted by means of one of the largest collections of pseudoscientific health literature ever assembled. A seizure in Washington, D.C., included more than 100 different leaflets, books, booklets, reprints, manuals, recordings, filmstrips, sales kits, recruiting kits, etc.

"Directly and indirectly, Nutri-Bio was being recommended through this literature as the answer to practically all health problems—anemia, arthritis, cancer, diabetes, frigidity, heart trouble, infections, nervousness, and so on. Then on the positive side it promised health, beauty, athletic ability, radiant living, and the capacity to stay young and vital. It was even recommended as a cure for juvenile delinquency.

"The Nutri-Bio promotion was a classic example of food faddism gone wild. It would take several pages to list all the false claims and representations. Mushroom promotion methods had built it up to the point where more than 75,000 full and part-time sales agents were selling Nutri-Bio at $24 per package for a six-month supply for one person. The agents had to buy the sales literature as well as the products. Lured by the prospect of quick riches from the pyramid of chain-letter plan of distribution, many invested their life savings. For $10,000, for instance, you could start business as a 'general' and get maximum commissions on all sales by your subagents. The pyramid collapsed when the distributors realized that the District of Columbia case (brought against Nutri-Bio by the Federal government) was a challenge of the basic sales promotion materials and that they would be violating the law if they used them in their sales presentation. Nutri-Bio agents in the Chicago area alone turned in for destruction about 50 tons of this literature."

Another best-seller in the nutritional field—before the government cracked down on it—was Vitasafe brand vitamins and minerals capsules which were sold by mail order. Here the government seized nearly 4,000,000 pieces of not-so-subtle sales literature. Copy such as a photo of a husband and wife—with the husband asleep on the couch and the wife in anguish: "I'm worried—my husband's idea of a good time—sleeping all day Sunday."

Or another husband-and-wife scene, but now (after Vitasafe), the wife purrs: "Our fights have turned to kisses." Needless to say, Vitasafe sold like hot pills.

The court case that put Vitasafe out of business underscored the falsity in the often heard claim that nearly everybody suffers from some kind of vitamin or mineral deficiency because our food supply does not contain enough of these elements. As one expert witness put it: "When all the cases of vitamin deficiency reported in the United States in a single year are added up they do not reach the figure of 20,000, and therefore the clinically ascertainable incidence as manifested by published reports is much less than 1 per cent."

Drawing attention to the tons of promotional materials used by Nutrio-Bio and Vitasafe, Larrick pinpointed the difficulty of fighting nutritional quackery: "Compare this (volume) with the efforts of the government and voluntary health agencies to disseminate reliable information."

The government has, in fact, displayed diligence. But it does not seem to have the horses to catch the runaway promoters. Today, the elderly can still buy Nirvana, panacea, or

Methuselan longevity in a pill, a food, or a diet. Here is a brief sampling of some, which the government has been able to remove from the market. Many of their claims seem to be hardly changed from the spiel of the old-time snake-oil salesmen or medicine men. Others are more sophisticated. They have this in common, however: millions of America's aged fell for them—all lost their money and quite a few shortened their lives because they did. And if these same brands are no longer with us, others have quickly filled their place.

VISOL-VITAMIN PRODUCT: For strengthening vision and brain, for treatment and prevention of loss of eye brightness, for infection of the mucosa, and dryness of skin.

YERBA MATE: For producing exhilaration and relief from fatigue, stomach acidity, indigestion, and constipation; also claimed that it is a heart tonic and diuretic; that it will excite the brain to increased mental activity and capacity; stimulate organs of nutrition; comfort the mind and dispel weariness, insomnia, cerebral erethism, headache, dyspepsia; will counteract depression of alcoholic debauching, gout, nerve disorders, and others.

VI-RON-ITE TONIC: For treatment and prevention of anemia, rundown condition, and tiredness; to promote tissue growth, release body energy, slow down the aging process, retain blood-vessel pliability, build muscle and nerve tissues, and promote normal energy metabolism. Also claimed one bottle supplies as much essential iron as 40 pints of raw oysters, 9 pounds of beefsteak, 93 pounds of spinach, or 60 pounds of fish.

Super Coronaid Tablets: For prevention and management of arteriosclerosis, coronary heart attacks, and diseased arteries. Also suggested that its use may add years to your life, improve your health, reduce cholesterol in the arteries, save you from sudden heart attacks, and help keep your arteries flexible.

Natural vitamin C "400" tablets: For prevention of stiff joints, rheumatic pains, asthma, allergies, bleeding gums, hardening of the arteries, weak blood capillaries, slow wound healing, poor resistance to disease, lack of vitality, nutritional anemia.

Superamino Tablets: For prevention of great fatigue, loss of strength and pep, depression, and vague aches and pains; for promoting youthful strength, energy, firm healthy tissues; for gland repair, enzyme and hormone production, resistance to disease, vigorous health, body-building, to produce antibodies to fight disease, including infections, bacterial and virus diseases; for blood, long life, bone-cell and bone development, heart-tissue growth and heart-cycle action; and to maintain brain tissues in later life.

Oro-Vita Food Supplement: Claimed to contain a so-called triamin base represented as a unique, nutritional discovery consisting of elements from the land, the sea, and from what used to be the bottom of the sea, and that all of its trace elements interrelate and balance for near perfect function. Implied that it is effective for the treatment and prevention of numerous diseases and afflictions of the body, including irritability, low vitality, stunted growth, soft bones, malformed teeth

[69

which decay easily, fragile bones in old people, senility, premature aging, neuritis, senile dementia, chronic sickness, digestive, nervous and mental ailments, damage to the liver, coronary heart attacks, strokes, diseases of the kidney, premature wrinkles, intelligence loss, migraine headaches, obesity, diabetes, cancer, leukemia, memory defects, severe agitation, and pernicious anemia.

GOLD-N-SWEET SAFFLOWER SHORTENING: Implied it is effective in the prevention of arteriosclerosis, heart attacks, strokes, and for other purposes.

VITA-GLO FOOD SUPPLEMENT, AND NUTRA-GLO FOOD SUPPLEMENT: Implied to be effective for treatment of infections and improper functioning of all parts of the body, as well as for nervous disorders, anemia, and dental decay; and effective to promote growth and longevity.

DEHYDRATED CABBAGE TABLETS: Claimed to be of significant value as a special dietary supplement, and also suggested it is effective in the treatment of ulcers.

A-E PLUS CAPSULES: For infection of mucous membranes of eyes, nose, mouth and throat, treatment and prevention of a wide range of ills, protection against adverse changes in the body; to promote growth, healthy eyes, and skin; that the germ oil and lecithin in the product will promote significantly the absorption of vitamins A and E; and that the lecithin in it will promote fat digestion and fat transport in the body, particularly for people over forty.

SPEED-A-VITE CAPSULES: Implied to be effective for the treatment and prevention of infection of the mucous membranes of eyes, nose, mouth and throat, and in promoting healthy eyes and skin.

SAFINOL CAPSULES: For dissolving fat, promoting fat transportation in the body, building the blood, and for the promoting of all functions of the body.

SOYBEAN LECITHIN: For promoting fat digestion and fat transport in the body, particularly for people over forty.

ADMIRAL SEA SPRAY SALT: Claimed to contain all the trace elements from the sea, which are catalysts that unlock the benefits of food so that the body can utilize such food to best advantage.

REPLENZ: For aiding the digestive process, dyspepsia, food intolerance, belching, flatulence, "over 40 stomach troubles," stomach distress due to enzyne deficiency, gas heartburn, and lack of vitamins due to impaired intestinal absorption.

LIVER-IRON-VITAMINS: Claimed to be effective in the treatment of all types of anemia which respond to liver and iron salts.

VIT-RA-TOX COLO-CLENZ No. 19 AND VEICO No. 79A INTESTINAL CLEANER: Labeling on these two items implied that constipation is the universal disease; that less than two or three bowel movements a day results in poisoning of the body; that lack of bulk in the diet causes abnormal digestive processes, foul body odors, poisoning, interference with absorption of nutrients, and promotes diseases; and that the use of these products will correct all these conditions.

SPRINGREEN Nos. 30, 31, 33, 60: Labeling of these four products implied that the American diets are lacking in vital nutrients because many foods are deficient in their expected nutritional value due to depleted soils, refining, processing, transportation, and cooking, and that the use of Springreen is necessary to correct these deficiencies.

HEMO-GLO TABLETS: Promotion implied that this product is of significant value as a special dietary supplement, and for treatment of iron deficiency anemia because it contains black cohosh, bushu leaves, comfrey root, strawberry leaves, mullein leaves, violet leaves, pipssewa herb, juniper berries, licorice root, buckhorn bark, celluolytic enzyme, amylolutic enzyme, lipolytic enzyme, prickly ash bark, inositol, choline, lecithin, dulse, burdock root, dandelion root, Oregon grape root, yellow dock, gentian root, red clover blossom, hyssop, sarsaparilla root, watercress juice, alfalfa juice, rutin, lemon bioflavonoid, beef peptone, red bone marrow, and desiccated and defatted liver.

JETTUP B COMPLEX WITH B 12: Claimed to be effective for treatment of nervous tension, uncontrolled movements of the hands and legs, irritability, fast pulse, fatigue, loss of appetite, inability to sleep, swelling of the face and ankles, decrease in mental and physical efficiency, blurred vision, and irritation of the eyes, corners of the mouth and nostrils, and that it is unusually fast-acting in the treatment of disease.

GERIATRIC VITAMIN TABLETS: Claimed to have unusual

value as a special diet additive for the elderly because the nutritional requirements of the elderly are different from those of adults generally.

SUPRO-ZYME TABLETS: Claimed to be of use in treatment and prevention of tired-blood anemia, vague aches and pains, pneumonia, intestinal infections, improper heart functions, and arthritis.

BIOTTA JUICES (lacto-carrot, celery, and beet): Claimed to be effective in the treament and prevention of fatigue, obstipation, chronic disturbances of the gastrointestinal tract, unspecific dermatoses, nervous and overstrained conditions, obesity, rheumatism, cardiac conditions, and cancer.

MINERALIFE CAPSULES: Worthless rock material with false and misleading claims for the treatment of cancer, heart trouble, shortness of breath, and tiredness, along with the claim that the capsules will restore youthfulness and promote relaxation and calmness.

VARIOUS HEALTH TABLETS (MILLRUE, SOY GERM OIL, PHYL-IN-ALFA): Claimed to be effective in the treatment of breast malignancies, colitis, ulcers, piles, tumors, asthma, cysts, arthritis, and inoperable cancer.

5 | Cancer Cures: No Shortages

The Senate Sub-Committee on Frauds and Deceptions Against the Elderly, after sifting more than 1,000 pages of testimony, concluded: "Complexity of modern life and modern machines give the quack considerable opportunity to sow confusion."

A noted psychiatrist, in an address to the National Congress on Medical Quackery, noted: "The need to believe in a therapeutic miracle when medicine is, or seems to be, failing can be so strong that it drives one's intelligence into twisting the facts to fit emotional necessity."

Nowhere are these two factors more evident than in the

search by older people for cancer cures and the readiness by a variety of "doctors" to provide them.

According to the American Cancer Society, those who offer these cures are not necessarily unprincipled quacks. In its brochure, *Unproven Methods of Cancer Treatment,* it states: "The proponents of new or unproven methods of cancer management range from ignorant, uneducated, misguided persons to highly educated scientists with advanced degrees who are out of their area of competency in supporting a particular form of treatment."

The statement is on the charitable side. One would hardly call the inventors and peddlers of the Film-O-Sonic, an altered tape recorder whose electronic waves were supposed to cure cancer, anything but crooks.

In the last two hundred years, thousands of cancer cures have been promoted or sold in this country. Their methodologies range from Wilhelm Reich's Orgone energy (a box one sits in) to the "grape cure," which requires the patient to live exclusively on a diet of grapes or grape juice for specified periods of time.

Since the aged are, in many respects, a tightly knit community, the cancer huckster relies on advertising that stresses the successful cure of a neighbor or friend. That so many fall for their spiel is not surprising. Wily, parsimonious Benjamin Franklin swallowed the bait—hook, line, and sinker.

On June 10, 1731, he wrote to his sister, "I know cancer of the breast is often thought to be incurable, yet we have here in town a kind of shell made of some wood, cut at a proper time by some men of great skill, which has done wonders in this disease among us, being worn for some time on the breast. I am not apt to be superstitiously fond of believing such things, but the instances are so well attested as to convince the most incredulous."

Today, even our own judiciary can fall for testimonials. In the first trial of notorious quack Harry Hoxey (The "Hoxey" method) in Dallas, the United States district judge found that the Hoxey Cancer Clinic did, in fact, cure some people of cancer. What swayed the court was the testimony of "cured" witnesses. A higher court reversed this decision.

Hoxey and his clinics, which go back to the 1920's, are perhaps the all-time champs in an ever growing list of cancer cures.

According to Harry M. Hoxey and his book, *You Don't Have to Die,* his cure has been in his family for over a century and was given to him by his father. He describes his method of treating cancer as a combination of three elements: "internal medicine, external compounds and supportive treatment." The internal medicine, taken orally, is to "restore the body to physiological normalcy." The external medication is applied "in accordance with location and types of cancer." Among other things this powder contains arsenic sulfide, zinc chloride, and bloodroot.

Hoxey defines his methods as "essentially chemotherapy." Admitting that he does not know the cause of cancer, he goes on to claim that somehow the chemical imbalance in the body produced mutated cells which eventually evolve into the cancer cells. His "cure": "If the constitution of body fluids can be normalized and the original chemical imbalance in the body restored, the environment again will become unfavorable for the survival and reproduction of these cells. They will cease to multiply and eventually die. Then, if vital organs have not been too seriously damaged by the malignancy (or by surgery

or irradiation) the entire organism will recover normal health."
A neat package with just enough medical mumbo-jumbo to
sell elderly people a very high bill of goods.

Not taken in was the United States Food and Drug Administration, which found that the internal medicine was composed
chiefly of pepsin. According to the FDA, Hoxey was an old-
timer at selling patent medicines, even before he opened his
first clinic in 1936. The government agency revealed that
Hoxey had hawked medicine from state to state since the early
20's when it was known as the "Hoxide" treatment. In 1956,
the FDA Commissioner said: "Harry M. Hoxey has continued
to promote his worthless cure for more than thirty years, not-
withstanding numerous local and state court actions."

In the face of increasing pressure, Hoxey transferred the
Hoxey Cancer Clinic to Dr. Harry R. Taylor and it became the
Taylor Clinic. Finally in 1960, the FDA got a permanent in-
junction against the Taylor Clinic, which banned the sale of all
Hoxey medication and required Dr. Taylor to notify all patients
that treatment was no longer available.

During various trials, the government presented volumes of
scientific evidence which showed that Hoxey dealt with three
types of patients—none of whom ever found cures: (1) patients
who never had cancer; (2) patients who had been cured of
cancer before they went to the clinic; (3) patients who had
cancer and were never helped by the Hoxey treatment.

If the Hoxey treatment has, for the moment, faded from
the scene, new entrants in the cancer cure sweepstakes are still
running hard. From 1960 to 1965 a flood of books describing
breakthroughs against cancer appeared. Each has its own method
to sell. Among these are: *Has Dr. Max Gerson a True Cancer
Cure?; The Incredible Story of Krebiozen; A New Approach*

to the Conquest of Cancer, Rheumatic and Heart Disease; Laetrile: Control of Cancer; Diäitis, Anti-Cancer Nutrients in Cancer Prevention Cure.

Because of the understandable public interest in finding a cure for cancer, these books and others have received widespread and sensational publicity. Let us look behind the hoopla to the hard facts.

The Gerson method, which was used during Dr. Gerson's lifetime in his sanitorium near New York City, is basically that of diet. Initially, preparation of food in aluminum utensils is *verboten*. Principal ingredients of the regimen are liver, vitamins, fresh fruit and vegetables. The vegetables are turned into juices by special machines which cost patients $150. Enemas—including coffee enemas—are frequently prescribed.

Has Dr. Max Gerson A True Cancer Cure? is the title of the book which lays down these rules and regulations among others. A Committee of the New York County Medical Society which reviewed Dr. Gerson's work replied to the title with a resounding "NO!" According to these investigators, no scientific evidence existed to substantiate any claim that the Gerson method resulted in any improvement in patients.

These findings were released in 1947. They hardly put a crimp in Dr. Gerson's style. He continued to practice his treatment at Gotham Hospital until 1950 and to prescribe it from his Park Avenue office. Finally, on March 4, 1958, a year before his death, he was suspended for two years from the New York County Medical Society.

Was this the end of the Gerson miracle? Not at the Hidden Valley Ranch, Escondido, California, where the same method has been used. And if the Foundation for Cancer Treatment has its way many more cancer victims will have the dubious luck of receiving the Gerson touch.

This Foundation is described in Dr. Gerson's 1958 book, *A Cancer Therapy: Results of Fifty Cases* (reprinted in 1965 under the title, *A Cancer Therapy*) as a "nonprofit organization formed . . . by grateful patients for the purpose of perpetuating the treatment." Doctors interested in obtaining a franchise to use the treatment are urged to get in touch with the Foundation.

How many already have, or will, is anybody's guess. One thing is sure: the Gerson method lives—would that one could say the same about the majority of its patients.

The book, *Laetrile, Control for Cancer* tells the story of Dr. Ernst T. Krebs, Sr., and his discovery of Laetrile. In it Krebs claims: "Laetrile acts only upon cancer cells, with the result that when all cancer cells are destroyed there is still a tumor—but it is benign." Krebs goes on to say that as soon as tests show nonmalignancy "the surgeon should remove the benign growth." However, a maintenance dose of Laetrile is required throughout the patient's life.

Laetrile was manufactured and distributed by the John Beard Memorial Foundation which has described itself as "a nonprofit organization founded, privately owned, and maintained through the benefaction of the Krebs family . . . concerned with biological, biochemical and medical research."

A most laudable prospectus. However, this high-sounding language does not jibe with a report from the United States Food and Drug Administration, which reveals that Ernst T. Krebs, Jr., a biochemist, and the John Beard Memorial Foundation pleaded guilty in United States District Court, San Francisco, to five counts of violating the provisions of the Federal Food, Drug and Cosmetic Act. Krebs Jr., who was fined $3,755, received a suspended jail sentence and was placed on three years probation. The verdict also contained a provision prohibiting interstate shipment of Laetrile, before filing a new application with the FDA.

It is doubtful whether such permission will be granted since the FDA report on Laetrile plainly states that it has seen "no competent, scientific evidence that Laetrile is effective for the treatment of cancer."

But Krebs, Sr.—originator of Laetrile—decided to buck the FDA, to his regret. Thus, according to the agency's *Report on Enforcement and Compliance* (September, 1965), he had disobeyed the restraining order by shipping Laetrile to a hospital in Alabama and to doctors in Utah, Texas, and Washington.

Brought to trial on criminal contempt charges, he pleaded "no contest" and agreed to a permanent court injunction against further distribution of the drug. He told the court he was going out of business.

It was a short retirement. On January 21, 1966, Krebs Sr., pleaded guilty to a charge of contempt for shipping Laetrile in violation of an injunction. Two weeks later, in a California United States District Court, he was given a suspended sentence of one year for failure to register as a producer of drugs, specifically Laetrile.

Has Laetrile been laid to rest? Perhaps. Will it rise again? Look at its history.

Krebiozen: Of all the highly publicized cancer cures of the past decade, the Krebiozen story is the most sensational, the most confused, and the one that aroused the strongest passions.

The use and prescription of the drug resulted in the trial and acquittal of a distinguished scientist, Dr. Andrew Ivy, Professor Emeritus of the University of Illinois. Opinion on the drug ranged from the FDA Commissioner who described it as a cruel hoax and flatly asserted that "each day a person with treatable cancer relies upon Krebiozen is a day that brings him closer to death," to cancer victims who organized marches and demonstrations to dramatize their faith in Krebiozen's curative powers.

An FDA investigation of the records of the Krebiozen Foundation sifted through 4,307 patients with clinical cancer, who had been treated with the drug before 1962. Of these 2,781, records were judged unacceptable for evaluation because of overlapping treatment and other criteria. Of the remaining 1,573, three patients were found in whom it was possible, but not certain—that partial regression of a tumor could have resulted.

Subsequently, samples of Krebiozen, analyzed by the FDA, were found to be a normal constituent of muscle, *creatine monohydrate*, a common laboratory compound purchasable for approximately $10 an ounce.

To this the Krebiozen Foundation answered that the FDA had not, in fact, analyzed Krebiozen.

Following the thalidomide tragedy, the FDA's powers were broadened to require that all investigational drugs be subjected to registration. Under this new system three requirements must be met: (1) A plan of investigation must be filed; (2) competent investigators must be identified; (3) complete disclosure of manufacturing processes must be provided.

The Krebiozen Foundation did not choose to meet the requirements, and by not filing, lost its right to ship the drug from Illinois to any other state in the union.

The FDA followed up its fight with Krebiozen by bringing to trial—for violations of FDA regulations and fraud—Dr. Ivy and his associates, Dr. John Pick, Dr. Stevan Durovic, discoverer of the drug, and his brother, Marko Durovic. Acquittal by a jury came after eight days of deliberation.

However, Dr. Durovic's troubles with the law were not over. At the trial, government investigators showed that large sums derived from the sale of Krebiozen had been sent by him to Canadian and Swiss banks. Based on this information he was indicted for evasion of income tax in the amount of $904,907—a figure which dramatically reflects the gold to be mined in cancer cures.

In a cloak-and-dagger episode, Durovic slipped by internal revenue agents who had been alerted and were watching international airports. According to these agents, he flew from Miami to Bimini to Bermuda to London to Paris. He is currently reported to be in Switzerland undergoing treatment for tuberculosis. He says he does not owe the government anything and will return to Chicago as soon as he is well enough.

Although the Chicago jury found the main actors in the Krebiozen drama not guilty of fraud, the American Cancer Society has not changed its mind about Krebiozen. It states: "The verdict of the Chicago jury in no way alters the position of the American Cancer Society relative to the ineffectiveness of Krebiozen for the treatment of cancer."

The impact of the Krebiozen story and similar "cure" drugs was succinctly spelled out by Dr. James F. Holland, Director, Cancer Clinical Research Center, Roosevelt Park Memorial Institute in Buffalo, New York. Addressing the Third National Congress on Medical Quackery, he said:

"We must remember that the great tragedy of the Krebiozen myth is that it is a myth. Cancer still maims and kills. There are too few people in the world qualified and able to pursue cancer research to dissipate their energies on negative leads . . . The challenge of cancer is too important and pervasive for society and the scientific community to squander any more time on false lures or mineral oils."

Dr. Holland's admonitions may be well taken by members of the medical profession, nevertheless the myths of cancer cures continue unabated. And hundreds of quacks sell myths as a high-priced reality. A complete listing or lengthy description of all of these "cures" could fill volumes, however, a roll call of the more typical kinds of drugs and methods may serve as an early warning signal for the unwary.

KC-555 has been described as an "adjunctive treatment in malignant diseases." The FDA describes it as a "botanical extract derived from Asian-grown plants." It is taken in a highly imaginative way—by adding Chianti wine and bitters.

Livingston Vaccine, a pleuropneumonia-like organism prepared from cultures grown from the patient's urine and killed with phenol. It is administered by injection.

Hadley Vaccine (in conjunction with blood and skin tests) is "a blood test that shows the presence or absence of cancer which requires only a sample of blood and "a skin test which determines susceptibility to cancer." The Hadley vaccine has, according to its promoters "a beneficial effect in a period 5 to 10 years after the injection."

Heat Therapy has many variations. In a particularly dramatic one the patient is placed in a specially constructed bath. By use of hot water the temperature is raised to 107.6^0 or 111.2^0 in the cases of inoperable local tumors. The treatment varies in duration from 30 to 45 minutes and is supported by administration of a large dose of a special drug. According to the salesmen of this method, up to 95 per cent of cancer cells may be killed by this procedure.

Samuel's Causal Therapy claims cancer is caused by an imbalance of hormones secreted by the pituitary. The cure is short-wave irradiation of the pituitary or the sex glands. This is done with an "automatic short-wave apparatus."

The Nichols Method uses pastes of arsenical and/or zinc compounds. The main dispenser of this salve is the Savannah Cancer Clinic. According to some reports, application of this paste is so disfiguring as to require subsequent plastic surgery.

Multiple Enzyme Therapy is based on the theory that cancer is caused by an enzyme deficiency which allows new cells to grow without built-in enzymatic controls. Thus, intravenous injections of multiple enzymes will help the body cells overcome this deficiency.

The Grape Cure has been going for quite some time, as is evidenced by the twenty-first edition of the book entitled *The Grape Cure,* by Johanna Brandt. According to this method a grape meal, which can vary from two ounces to half a pound of any good variety of grapes is taken starting at 8 A.M., and repeated every two hours. All in all, seven meals of grapes a day. Only water is allowed in addition. Anticipating the obvious, the book states that if, after some days of this regimen, *a loathing for grapes develops,* it "indicates the need for a fast—skip a few meals." In any case, the exclusive grape diet is kept up for one or two weeks. Then comes the introduction of fresh fruits and sour milk followed by raw vegetables, salads, dried fruits, nuts, milk products, and olive oil. Eventually, under favorable circumstances, the patient is allowed one cooked meal at midday. This diet is being used to fight cancer by drugless practitioners and health spas. The grape products are often procured from health-food stores.

Anticancergen Z-50 is the concoction of George S. Zuccala, who claims that human cells, including cancer, produce an unknown substance called "motivana" which has the ability to sensitize other body cells. These cells become incapable of resisting the disease, which therefore progresses. He has developed the Zuccala Lytic Test to detect this phenomenon and the Anticancergen Z-50 to prevent sensitization of the body cells and cancer.

Icador is a preparation made from various kinds of mistletoe and is the discovery of Dr. Rudolph Steiner, founder of the Society for Cancer Research of Switzerland. Various types of mistletoe are used in this preparation. Also, according to a 1962 report of the Society: "It is necessary to pay attention to the time of picking . . . we are interested in its toxicity, its acidity and above all the inequality of the sap." Believers in this method find that the plants "not only react to the influences of sun and moon but also to those of the planets." And finally: "As sun, moon and planets move on regular paths . . . the right times to pick can be calculated months beforehand. This is also important as the places where the mistletoe has to be picked often lie many hundreds of miles away."

The Spears Hygenic System based on the Spears Painless System of Chiropractic, is used to treat many diseases and conditions at the Spears Chiropractic Hospital in Denver, Colorado. The system treats cancer by adjusting the segments of the spine . . . by colon irrigation . . . by nerve-cell goading and reflex techniques . . . by spinal and other forms of traction . . . by physiotherapy and correctional exercises . . . and by diet to give the required nutrition.

[85

Antineol is a preparation extracted from the pituitary glands of cattle.

The Koch Treatment holds that cancer is a protective response to a toxic product generated within the body and which can be countered by using a cleansing diet in combination with three Koch antitoxins. The treatment was prevalent in the United States from about 1926 until 1948 when, following government inspection of the Koch Laboratories in Detroit, it went out of business. The founder, Dr. Koch, then moved to Brazil where he opened a new laboratory. His antitoxins are still being marketed in this country.

The Revici Cancer Control or Lipid Therapy is based on the theory that cancer is the product of imbalance between acid and alkaline in the tissues. After determining the kind of imbalance present, patients are treated through the administration of Lipids which promote either an acid or alkaline reaction. Dr. Revici describes this treatment as "biologically guided chemotherapy."

Mucorhican is produced by the cultivation of a mold on a nutrient composed of yeast, salt, whole wheat, and sterile water. It is dispensed by the Nutrition Service, Inc. of Pittsburgh, Pennsylvania, and is "administered orally only in conjunction with diet." This diet allows many foods, but only country butter and unprocessed cheese may be used. At a hearing in the United States District Court in Pittsburgh in 1964, the manufacturers of Mucorhican sought to prevent an FDA injunction by stating that it is a food product or adjunct rather than a drug. It was claimed that more than four hundred doctors in the United States had been prescribing it.

H. H. Beard Methods are described in the book *A New Approach to the Conquest of Cancer, Rheumatic and Heart*

Diseases by Howard H. Beard. Three biological tests have been developed by Beard for the diagnosis of cancer. The first was a Laboratory Urine Test which would show whether cancer was present in any part of the body. Next Beard worked on a Milk Assay Test based on the slower clotting of milk when malignant urine was added, for which 95 per cent diagnostic accuracy was claimed. Finally, he came up with the Anthrone Color Test, which is based on measuring the amount of a sex hormone found in the urine. These tests, and the therapies based upon them, stem from his thesis which states that "the wandering germ cells of early life can be activated to divide and produce trophilblast cells which, outside the canalization of pregnancy, are malignant cells. The cure is an injection which "stops all tumor respiration." A diet is also prescribed.

The Frost Method employs special vaccines, diet, and the Koch antitoxins, Krebiozen and Mucorhican.

Diamond Carbon Compound was developed in Bombay, India, and is basically the oral administration of capsules composed of crystals of pure diamonds and other substances. The price of eighty capsules, enough for a basic treatment, is $1,180. According to promotional literature, manufacture of the drug by hand requires almost a full month and accounts for its high cost.

Fresh Cell Therapy has at one time or another reportedly restored youth to such public figures as the late Chancellor Konrad Adenauer of West Germany. Treatment is by injection of fresh embryonic animal cells of the organ or tissue believed to be causing the illness in the human patient. A special diet is also recommended.

Coley's Mixed Toxins include thirteen different products in which different strains of streptococci are used.

Carzodelan is an enzyme preparation claimed to be capable of dissolving tumors. Along with this drug the patient must remain on a special nonanimal-fat diet.

In addition to those internal medications, numerous unscientific and bizarre machines and devices have been promoted for the diagnosis, treatment, or cure of cancer.

These have ranged from the simple Vrilium Tube or "magic spike" containing a penny's worth of barium chloride, to the impressive Detoxacolon machine, sold to chiropractors and naturopaths for $2,500 in a package deal, which guaranteed the practitioner a booming business by advertising a clinic for free "physical examinations."

The Detoxacolon did little more than irrigate the colon under pressure. The chiropractor who promoted it made more than $500,000.

The Orgone Energy Accumulator, a zinc-lined box in which the patient sat to absorb "orgone energy" was promoted by a discredited psychoanalyst who died in prison.

A whole series of devices form the Drown Instruments, developed by Ruth Drown, a chiropractor, who died in 1965. Proponents claimed that a sample of a patient's blood on a piece of blotting paper could be placed in the device, and from this, the patient's condition was diagnosed. Treatments then could be transmitted through the air to the patient even in another state.

In 1966, two Los Angeles women were convicted of grand theft charges involving Drown Instruments, used to "diagnose" and "treat" diseases ranging from cancer and heart trouble to kidney infections and head colds.

Other absurd devices have been widely sold or used for cancer treatment. Promoters of one device—the Spectro-Chrome—claimed it could "cure" cancer by bathing the affected part of the body in colored light. Purple and blue were for cancer; red and purple for heart disease. Another device—the Sonus Film-O-Sonic—featured tape-recorded music and electrode pads attached to the patient. The melody "Smoke Gets in Your Eyes" was supposed to cure cancer; "Holiday for Strings" was for arteriosclerosis.

We will meet many more of these therapeutic monsters in the next chapter.

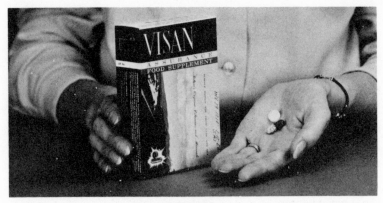

VISAN

A diet fad, vitamin product, Visan was offered as beneficial for arthritis. Medical science has disapproved theories that particular foods have specific effects on arthritis.

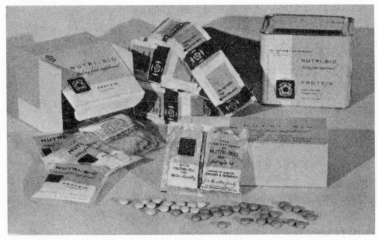

Food supplements seized for fraudulent claims made by advertisements and salesmen.

Safflower oil capsules used in a weight control program were taken off the market due to false claims.

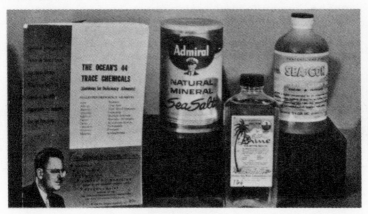

Sea water swindle—high prices were charged for ordinary minerals that are abundant in any balanced diet.

Public
Beware!

WARNING AGAINST THE HOXSEY CANCER TREATMENT

Sufferers from cancer, their families, physicians, and all concerned with the care of cancer patients are hereby advised and warned that the Hoxsey treatment for internal cancer has been found worthless by two Federal courts

The Hoxsey treatment costs $400, plus $60 in additional fees—expenditures which will yield nothing of value in the care of cancer. It consists essentially of simple drugs which are worthless for treating cancer.

The Food and Drug Administration conducted a thorough investigation of the Hoxsey treatment and the cases which were claimed to be cured. Not a single verified cure of internal cancer by this treatment has been found.

Those afflicted with cancer are warned not to be misled by the false promise that the Hoxsey cancer treatment will cure or alleviate their condition. Cancer can be cured only through surgery or radiation. Death from cancer is inevitable when cancer patients fail to obtain proper medical treatment because of the lure of a painless cure "without the use of surgery, x-ray, or radium" as claimed by Hoxsey.

Anyone planning to try this treatment should get the facts about it.

For further information write to:
U. S. DEPARTMENT OF HEALTH, EDUCATION, AND WELFARE
Food and Drug Administration
Washington 25, D. C.

Warning by the U. S. Department of Health, Education and Welfare regarding the Hoxsey cancer "treatment."

MAGNETRON

By plugging in this device, placing one foot on the footpad, and holding the electrode in his hand, the patient was claimed to be helped for failing heart, enlarged prostate gland, diabetes, and asthma. The effects were purported to be the same for these conditions as antibiotics for infectious diseases. This mechanism sold for $195.

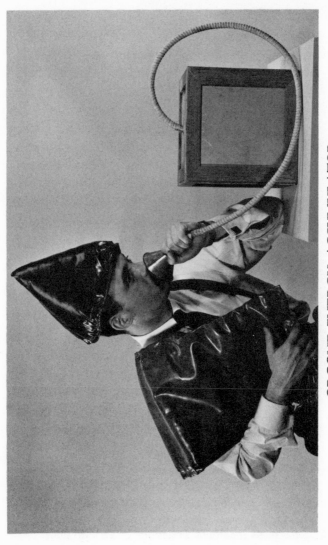

ORGONE ENERGY ACCUMULATOR

Pictured here is a person taking an infusion of "orgone energy." The inventor, Dr. Wilhelm Reich, was a brilliant psychiatrist before entering the hocuspocus world of medical gadgetry.

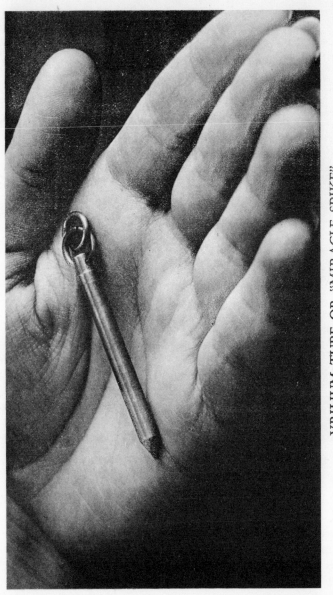

VRILIUM TUBE OR "MIRACLE SPIKE"

Arthritis sufferers paid $300 plus tax for this tube! Its contents of 1.2000th of a cent of barium chloride has no effect on the disease it claimed to cure.

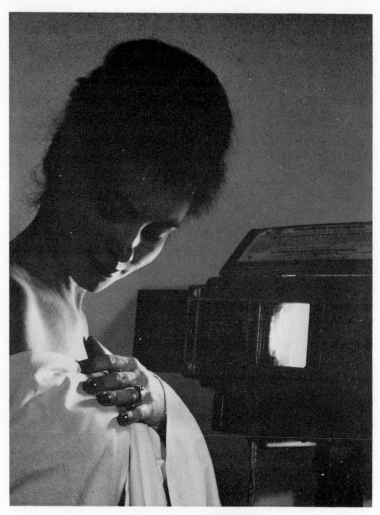

SPECTROCHROME

This device allegedly cured diseases by playing different-colored lights on afflicted areas during certain phases of the moon while the patient was in the dark, nude, with hands pointing north. A federal court order was issued in 1958 discontinuing the sale of this gadget.

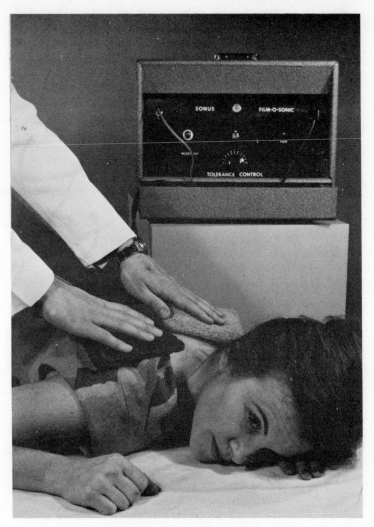

SONUS FILM-O-SONIC

By "silently" playing a recording of "Smoke Gets in Your Eyes", this device was supposed to cure cancer and sold for as high as $500. In court, the company agreed to a default decree.

6 | Therapeutic Devices: A Chamber of Horrors

In 1796, Dr. Elisha Perkins patented his "metallic tractors," making him the first man in the United States to exploit magnetism and electricty in treating the sick. His device consisted of two pointed magnetic rods two to three inches long. By putting them over the affected area of the body, the disease would be yanked out.

That this was considered a plausible theory is evidenced by the fact that a Chief Justice of the United States Supreme Court and many other prominent individuals underwent Perkins' treatment.

Even though Perkins' rods and imitations which followed are absolutely worthless, devices based on the same theory persist today. Magnetic belts and magnetic bracelets, to mention just two, continue to be hawked by quacks.

Through the eighteenth and nineteenth centuries, electricity and magnetism were promoted to cure everything from arthritis to lost manhood, but it was not until the early part of the twentieth century that device quackery found its true messiah. He was Dr. Albert Abrams of San Francisco who was characterized by Dr. Arthur J. Cramp, Director of the American Medical Association's Propaganda Division (subsequently its Department of Investigation) as the "dean of all twentieth-century charlatans."

Cashing in on the popularity of radio, which was then beginning to thrill the nation, Abrams wrote, in 1922: "The spirit of the age is radio, and we can use radio in diagnosis." He evolved a system of "radionics," based on the theory that electrons in all of us vibrate at a definite rate for every disease, therefore all disease is a "disharmony of electronic oscillation."

Developing both diagnostic and treatment devices—before there was a federal law controlling such instruments—he operated under the name of the "College of Electronic Medicine." Through his "College," Abrams pushed many devices, but his staple was the Oscilloclast, which treated all disease "by definite rates of vibration." He claimed that by matching the disease "vibrations" with those of the Oscilloclast the disease would be canceled out.

The patient did not have to be present for an Abrams diagnosis. He merely sent in a drop of blood on a blotter for placement in the Oscilloclast. The diagnosis cost $10—payable in advance.

Blotters and checks came to Dr. Abrams from every section of the country. In addition, Abrams rented Oscilloclasts to other doctors. At one point, some 4,000 practitioners were thought to be using the device.

Suspicious medical men began puncturing Abrams' ballooning business. One physician sent in a sample of rooster blood which Abrams diagnosed as belonging to a patient having diabetes, malaria, cancer, and syphilis. Another submitted blood from an amputee and received a diagnosis of arthritis of a right foot and ankle the man did not possess.

An investigation by a panel of scientists concluded that, "analyzed in the cold light of scientific knowledge, the entire Abrams matter is the height of absurdity . . . at best it is an illusion. At worst it is a colossal fraud."

Abrams died of pneumonia in 1924. He left an estate valued at $2,000,000.

Following Abram's death, his clinic and other interests were taken over by Fred Hart, a man of no scientific training, who operated as the Electronic Medical Foundation. Hart placed hundreds of expensive diagnostic and treatment devices in the offices of practitioners throughout the country, where they are still being used. The *modus operandi* was not much different from Abrams' method: The practitioner would mail a sample of blood on a blotter to the San Francisco clinic where it would be placed in a device called the "Radioscope" which was supposed to measure the "emanations" associated with different diseases given off by the dried blood. Readings from this machine were sent back to the practitioner, telling him the disease his patient was supposed to have and the type of treatment to be given by one of thirteen different machines the practitioner had previously purchased—none of which had any therapeutic value.

Following a series of court actions by the FDA against Hart in which the government agency proved—among other things—that his diagnostic machines could not tell the difference between blood from a living and dead man or between blood and colored water, his Electronic Medical Foundation was dissolved. But Hart, who has founded the National Health Federation in Monrovia, California, and a host of other medical gadgeteers still hawk their hope for the hopeless and cures for the incurable. Recently they have sold radioactive earth, combs, and pillows as cures for cancer. One imaginative operator put chairs in an old abandoned uranium mine and charged so much per hour to sit there. Long lines of elderly people sat with their feet in the "miraculous" earth.

The majority of quacks, however, still prefer gimmicks which are less earthbound. They "invent" more portable diagnostic and therapeutic devices which, when "used properly," can cure anything from rupture to polio. The machines look very impressive with dials, flashing lights, flickering needles, charts, and impressive console cabinets. In many cases they are deliberately designed to look like an X-ray machine, an electrocardiograph, or some other genuine scientific device.

One group that has gained considerable popularity involved generators that created ozone. The Calozone Ozone Generator, also known as Vitazone, Purozone, Orozone, Nevozone, and Airozone, were the most widely distributed phony devices ever investigated by the FDA.

At one time, there were over a hundred agents and subagents selling these devices in California as well as twenty other agents in twelve other states.

In one three-year period over 3,000 of these worthless machines were sold in California alone at $150 each. Touted as "God's gift to humanity," it was recommended for use in forty-seven diseases and conditions ranging from abcesses to whooping cough, cancer, tuberculosis, diabetes, heart disease, and polio.

Competent medical authorities testified that it was not only worthless as a therapeutic instrument but could be dangerous because of its output of up to thirty parts per million of ozone, three inches above the tubes. A demonstration showed that it would kill mice in a matter of hours. This hazard did not stop the promoters from inducing an aged doctor to write a booklet advocating the use of the device in the treatment of thirty-seven diseases. In addition, they published a series of so-called lectures entitled "Ozone—God's Gift to Humanity," misquoting eminent toxicologists, physicians, and medical authorities, advocating the use of ozone in the treatment of disease.

A similar device, an earlier model of ozone generator, was called the Ultraviolet Ray and Radiation Machine. Although an ultraviolet radiation effect was claimed, in actual fact the ultraviolet output was only equal to the output of an ordinary 40-watt light globe; hence the only active principle was the ozone produced.

Another larger and more expensive ozone generator, known as the Cosmic Light Ozone Generator, was sold for $300 each. During a three year period one quack sold $30,000 worth of these worthless and potentially dangerous devices. He also used them in conjunction with minerals, vitamins, and lotions in giving treatments to hundreds of patients for all kinds of diseases and ailments, including cancer, diabetes, insanity, gallstones, goiters, and varicose veins.

One of his specialties was diagnosing nonexistent vaginal tumors. He treated these women with the ozone machine in conjunction with drugs taken internally and finally with suppositories containing ferric and aluminum sulfates, which caused the vaginal wall to slough off. When this occurred he would assure them that these were ejected tumors.

As a sideline, this quack also manufactured an ointment or paste from dirt, which he used indiscriminately for the treatment of varicose veins, as a beauty cream and a hair restorer.

Another popular type of device is the so-called *Radionic Group*. These include:

Mark Gallert Research Laboratories: Gallert falsely represented himself as a radionic expert and naturopath. He claimed that his device—which sold for $545—could diagnose and treat tumors, cancer, syphilis, and all other diseases. It was constructed along the general lines of other radionic devices, consisting of a panel mounted with numerous switches all connected in series. The only true electrical circuit was the one which plugged directly into an AC house current to operate the various colored lights.

Gallert deviated from the usual radionic hocus-pocus by incorporating the zodiac. He was arrested by an FDA inspector who had received a diagnosis of "cancer of the liver, a tumor pressing on the heart, syphilis and lymphogranuloma." Charged with false advertising, misbranding, practicing medicine without a license, and petty theft, Gallert was placed on two years probation following a plea of guilty.

According to the FDA, in less than three months of activity in San Francisco, Gallert had developed an extensive clientele in addition to selling devices to members of a branch of the healing arts.

McCoy Device: McCoy, an oil dealer, made his diagnosis from the patient's signature. After the diagnosis, the self-styled "oscilloclast" was rented to the patient for $1 a day. The usual course of treatment was of sixty to ninety days' duration and was terminated after the patient's signature indicated he was cured.

There was an additional charge of $2 for each individual diagnostic service, including rechecks. Of the numerous patients treated by this quack, who falsely alleged himself to be a naturopath, nearly all were informed by him that they had cancer.

In addition to McCoy, several other individuals were found to be using this type of device.

Thermo-Ray Lamp: This lamp was sold as a cure-all, with particular emphasis on cancer. Its inventor applied for and received a patent for an infra-red lamp. After becoming associated with a masseur, his sales boomed. They advertised the lamp through practitioners of the healing arts. It sold for $185.

Electro Metabograph Diagnostic Machine and Quantumeter: These devices were seized from the office of John S. Newfield, a self-styled medical practitioner.

"Dr." Newfield, who holds no type of license to practice any of the healing arts, was arrested after he "diagnosed" one of the investigators by use of this machine as having heart disease and other serious ailments. After the diagnosis he offered to sell the investigator one of two quantumeters for treating the maladies—an old model for $195 or a newer model for $250.

Investigation and examination of his records disclosed that this charlatan had numerous patients from as far away as Phoenix, Arizona, and had collected as much as $1,500 in fees from some. He also had sold some thirty or forty quantu-meters for treating patients in their homes.

Analyzer and Energizer Devices: The analyzer (the larger of the two) was used to diagnose such ailments as cancer, ulcers of the stomach, heart and vascular diseases. Mechanically, this device consists of three circuits with two light bulbs and a warm plate which was stroked by the operator to arrive at a diagnosis. The smaller of the two devices, popularly known as an energizer, which sold for $100, consisted of an electric coil, a copper disk, and a couple of pounds of tar.

Chandler Diagnostic Device: This device, constructed by Gordon Chandler, a chiropractor, was used in 50 per cent of his cases to determine physical ailments. He stated that it established rapport between doctor and patient. He told one of his patients, a policewoman, that she had low blood energy, an alkaline colon, and weak optic nerves. One patient paid $135 for companion device treatments and vitamins for an acid bladder and thyroid condition which never existed.

Radiumator Device: This device was represented as a machine capable of producing radioactive water which would cure heart disease, high blood pressure, kidney disease, (including uremic poisoning), sexual debility, and abnormal metabolism. It was purported by the vendor that its therapeutic effect was brought about by the interaction of alpha and beta rays, causing a stimulative oxidation in adjacent animal or plant tissue; that the alpha ray—the principal component of radium gas, taken in the body, was constructive or healing in nature, whereas the gamma ray was destructive. The charlatans said that the device contained from $4,000 to $6,000 worth of pure radium chloride, whereas an analysis by a competent electronics laboratory revealed it to contain about $1.30 worth of radium.

Uranium Centers: A series of uranium treatment "centers" set up throughout northern California consisted of cubicles lined with low-grade uranium ore. Some had a series of beds with trays of uranium ore under them. The uranium ore used had a very low radiation emission—less than that of a common radium dial watch.

Sinusitis, arthritis, and many other diseases were treated at these "centers." Treatments consisted of an hour exposure to the uranium ore. The fee was usually $2 per treatment.

Besides Ozone, and Radionics, the elderly are sold a wide range of worthless devices, salves, and cure-alls.

Magic Cure-All Jug: The device consisted of an ordinary two-gallon size picnic jug with a silver-like bell at the lower end of a rod whose tap was connected to the lid. When the jug was filled with ordinary tap water and the bell immersed in it for twelve hours, the resulting "radium-impregnated" liquid, when taken internally, was guaranteed to cure almost any ailment including cancer, rheumatic fever, restore hair to bald heads, and revive virility.

The manufacturer bragged that some 9,000 generators had been sold in the United States during the past twenty years.

The salesman of the magic generators sold one for $300 to an inspector posing as the the brother of an actual cancer victim.

Laboratory analysis of the "bell' revealed it to contain a minute amount of radium mixed with iron oxide. However, it was of sufficient strength to cause the water in which it was suspended to be 305 times the maximum permissible safe concentration of radioactivity in water for continuous use.

Uranium Ray Pad: This pad, consisting of a leatherette bag filled with crushed rock which possessed slight radioactivity, was sold for $75 each. The purveyors claimed that it would cure sinusitis and arthritis. One elderly woman became so ill the manager of the hotel where she resided called a competent physician who recognized her condition as advancd tuberculosis.

Sinus Cure: One health-food faddist ran an ad in newspapers touting a sinus cure. Treatment instructions would be mailed from the promoter c.o.d. for a two-week course at $8.40. The person falling for the gimmick would receive a package of Knox Gelatin purchased from a store for 40 cents.

Herbs and Mallet: One Santa Cruz, California sharpie sold herbs which he claimed were effective for impotence and diseases, such as diabetes and cancer. He also sold a rubber mallet that was to be used in percussing certain areas of the body in effecting a cure for diabetes and cancer.

Juicer: It was claimed that this juicer possessed outstanding characteristics which rendered the juice derived from it of particular value in the treatment of diseases.

A booklet was used in connection with the sale of the machine recommending individual juices for specific diseases. For example, carrot juice was prescribed for the treatment of ulcers and cancer.

Investigation revealed that the juicer was an ordinary kitchen appliance that could impart no magical or extraordinary powers and added nothing to its product that would give it therapeutic value.

This juicer sold for about $100.

Electronic Steel Ball: This gimmick was an ordinary steel ball bearing, about three-fourths of an inch in diameter, which was represented by the vendor, Allen Daniel, to be energized with 81,000 volts of electricity. Patients were told that this device would permanently cure pain, particularly in neurotic and nervous patients. After being energized, the steel ball was grounded before being passed over the ailing part of the body. The inventor, a professed radio technician, was charged with the sale of a misbranded device and was successfully prosecuted.

Diagnostic Office: A diagnostic office advertised in newspapers offering a complete physical examination for $5. Their records showed that 650 persons were attracted and subsequently were given an extensive course of treatments and medications. Ninety-three per cent of these persons received the same diagnosis from the operators of this clinic, i.e., to have an enlarged heart and liver, a jellied gallbladder, and a high acid and bile condition, whereas scientific physical examinations disclosed that they were normal.

Rupture Cure: A former used-car salesman represented himself as a rupture specialist. His method of operation was to run advance ads in newspapers: "New sensational rupture development, no surgery, no injections, no more experiments with wrong trusses, instant relief, come in and leave with no more rupture trouble."

Actually he would fit an inexpensive $3.90 truss for which he would charge $75, claiming it was his own patented device with special pads.

Hemorrhoid Cures: There are, throughout the nation, many advertisements for hemorrhoid cures without surgery.

One such healer, a chiropractor, offered a nonsurgical cure for $150, using a bank time-payment plan.

A food and drug inspector, not suffering from hemorrhoids, obtained an examination. He was told that he had severe internal hemorrhoids with a lesion the size of a nickel that would likely develop into cancer unless his treatment was taken immediately.

He was offered easy time payments. After preparation and sale of a simple compound consisting of zinc oxide, starch, and carbolic acid, the quack was arrested and subsequently convicted on two counts of misbranding.

Coccidex: Coccidex was a purported cure for coccidioidomy-cosis—more commonly known as valley fever. A box of sixteen capsules, containing a mixture of sulfur, cocoa, charcoal, traces of ferrous sulfate and manganese dioxide—costing a few cents—sold for $5.

Cancer Salve: Two salves, both containing croton oil were used to treat internal and external cancer. Both salves were applied externally and were capable only of causing severe blisters and burning of the skin.

The quack offered to cure cancer of the stomach for $500. He stated that the formula for his product was a family secret and that the ingredient which did the actual curative work was one that "disappeared when added to the mixtures."

Pearly Savely Cancer Salve: Another con man used a con-coction of bloodroot, galingale root, and zinc chloride.

This quack claimed he could diagnose cancer by applying the salve to the suspected spot. If the salve affected the skin it was cancer, and he would continue to apply the salve until a sizable piece of burned flesh would separate from the surrounding flesh. Naturally, the salve had a strong corrosive and caustic action on any flesh, acting much in the manner of a powerful corn plaster.

Any victim who came to him with a skin blemish, mole, or wart of any kind, would be told he was suffering from cancer and would eventually lose some portion of his anatomy.

He had several jars of various-sized pieces of flesh preserved in alcohol which he boasted were cancers he had removed from people. He added that if he had saved all the cancers he had removed from people in over fifty-eight years of practice, they would fill a washtub.

Some of the specimens from the jars were examined by a pathologist who said he could find no evidence of cancer.

After diagnosing and treating a small mole on the shoulder of a volunteer operative as a "mole cancer," the quack was arrested.

A ROUNDUP OF FRAUDULENT CURES

Shown here are (rear row, L. to R.): Davis & Kidder's
Magneto Electric Device for nervous disorders; Ellis Micro-
Dynameter; Hoxsey Tonic; Peruna; Hadacol. Front row
(L. to R.): Lady Bountiful, an alleged breast developer;
Radithor, a drinking water irradiator; Sea Brine, plain sea
water; nasal apparatus and a vial of Lincoln bacteriophage.
Lower left front: Electro-Galvanic Bracelet.

THE ATOMOTRONE

This hoax was recommended for the treatment of serious diseases, including apoplexy, tumors, and ulcers. This device sold for $300, and its inventor was arrested for the illegal practice of medicine in Florida and Illinois.

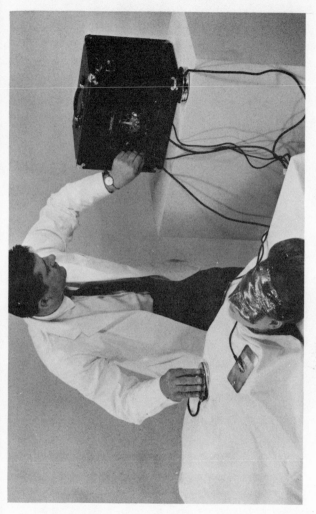

OSCILLOCLAST

The masked patient is having radio waves of the same frequency as the body's "evil emmission" neutralized by Dr. Albert Abrams' gadget. This immense commercial success failed to cure anything.

INFRA RAY THERAPEUTIC MITTENS
These mittens warm up when plugged into an electrical outlet, and were falsely claimed to help arthritis, sinus conditions, nervous disorders, and other ailments. They were condemned by court order.

POLERTON
Resembling a Chinese back scratcher, this device was used for treating many diseases. The machine was condemned, and taken off the market.

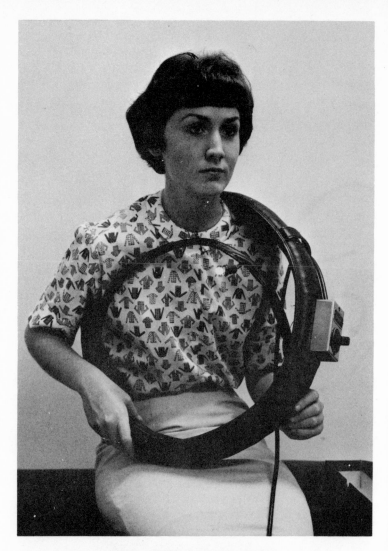

THE THERONOID BELT

The promoters claimed it was a cure-all which worked by magnetizing the iron of the blood. The photo shows a two-speed switch for effecting a slow or a gradual cure. It was seized by the Federal Trade Commission.

AIR-OZONE
When plugged in, the eight tubes of this device glow and
emit light energy of various wave lengths, producing ozone,
purported to provide effective treatment for angina pectoris,
arthritis, arterio-sclerosis, tuberculosis, and 37 other diseases.
The FDA seized this apparatus, and it was condemned by
court order.

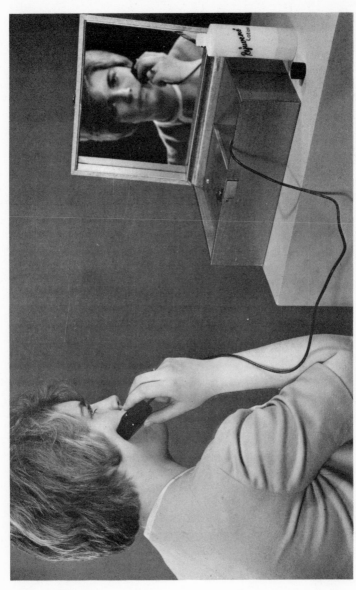

REJUVENE

This battery-operated applicator and lotion was claimed
to give knife-less face lifts and cure acne.

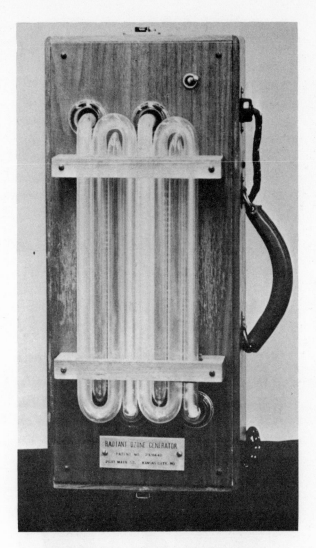

RADIANT OZONE GENERATOR

"Just Turn It On . . . and let ozone cure your arthritis," read
the ad for this fraudulent machine called the ozonator. It
gave off a pleasant odor, but did nothing for arthritis.
Price: $40.

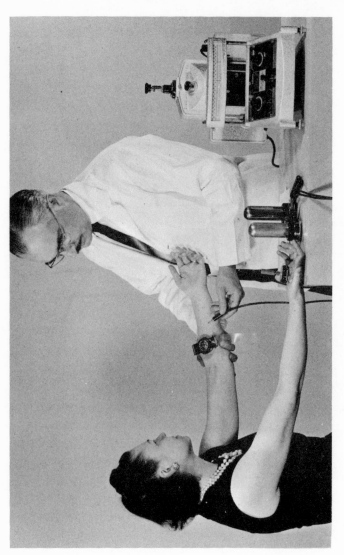

MICRO-DYNAMETER
Chiropractors purchased 5000 of these devices, purported to diagnose ailments. This machine only measures the moisture of the patient's skin. Price: $875.

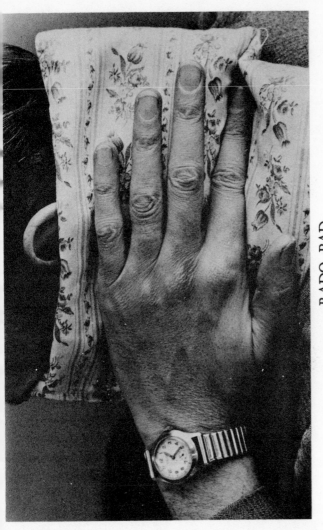

RADO PAD

One example of dozens of "uranium" gadgets claiming to help sufferers from arthritis, rheumatism, sinus and muscular ailments, this pad contained approximately the amount of radioactivity found in the luminous dial of a watch.

RADON GENERATOR

A device which gives off small amounts of radon, a gas. This gas was to be added to a jug of tap water. The claim was that if one drank two quarts of this water a day for a certain period of time, he would be cured of whatever disease he had. The device sold for $300 and could be purchased through a bank loan.

Advertisements for worthless treatment of prostatitis.

[123

7 | Hearing Aids: Many Do Not Help

Testimony before the Senate Subcommittee on Consumer Interests of the Elderly held in the summer of 1968 established the fact that hearing loss significantly restricts 30 to 50 per cent of the population past sixty-five years of age. Yet a survey by the Public Health Service revealed that nearly 53 per cent of hearing aid users over sixty-five have never had an autometric examination before buying a hearing aid.

Present-day clinical facilities can accommodate only about 10 per cent of all persons buying a hearing aid each year. There are almost 100 major urban centers in the United States with no established hearing services.

All this adds up to fertile ground for unscrupulous operators. In the words of Subcommittee Chairman Senator Frank Church of Idaho: "It is not the prime purpose of this Subcommittee to investigate . . . sharp practices. Yet we cannot ignore evidence of widespread door-to-door activity by salesman who obviously ignore all standards sought by responsible organizations and individuals . . . We should recognize the fact that the elderly are prime victims . . . of unscrupulous fast-moving salesman who are apparently still very active."

Senator Church cited information from the office of the Attorney General of California which told of the salesmen who carry their own "testing devices" and try to make on-the-spot sales, sometimes prescribing individual devices for each ear.

The Idaho Senator also read into the record some correspondence to the Subcommittee from elderly persons. One excerpt is typical of many complaints:

"They collect the down payment and have them sign a note which they sell to some finance company. When the aid is found to be of no benefit they pretend that they cannot make refund as promised in the first place but will make some change, geneerally trading one second-hand aid they have promised to sell for someone and just keep stalling until the elderly person gets disgusted and just lets it ride. They generally collect $300 for an aid. In the first place, the price is outrageous and the help one gets is very unsatisfactory. My wife got hooked for $600. They make all kinds of promises and keep none of them once they get their hands on the money which they demand in advance."

Although the code of ethics for the hearing-aid industry

adopted by the National Hearing Aid Society is a stringent one, it hardly has the force of law. In fact, only four states have some form of legislation regulating the practices of hearing aid dealers. A recent case heard by the Federal Trade Commission points up the opportunities for misrepresentation which exist in the field. Advertisements and other literature made grandiose promises for a product which the FTC found rather wanting in performance.

Representation: " ... each X is fully guaranteed ... there is a full refund if it does not give complete satisfaction."

FTC fact: The hearing aid is not unconditionally guaranteed, nor is the full purchase price refunded in all cases of dissatisfaction.

Representation: "For many years a scientist with the United States National Aeronautical Space Administration (NASA), Mr. Y (an officer of the corporation) was responsible for the development of the Molecular Amplifier for Space Capsules of Project Mercury."

FTC fact: Mr. Y was never employed by NASA, nor did he have any part in the development of equipment for Project Mercury Space Capsules.

Representation: "No batteries are used in X . . . the Power Generator is a permanent device which never needs replacement. X is powered by a Thermocell (which can make it) operate indefinitely with heat from your body."

FTC fact: The power source of X is a cadmium-cell battery which must be recharged at frequent intervals.

Representation: "When binaurally fitted it will correct losses up to 85 per cent."

FTC fact: However fitted the X will not substantially

improve the hearing of an individual with an 85 per cent hearing loss.

Representation: It covers easily up to a 65-decibel hearing loss without any feedback problem.

FTC fact: It will not substantially improve the hearing of an individual with a 65-decibel hearing loss. In fact, it will not improve hearing for individuals who have more than a minor hearing loss.

Representation: "Volume controlled automatically—the X has a built-in volume control."

FTC fact: It does not contain an automatic volume control.

Representation: "No distortion."

FTC fact: It will cause distortion of voices and other sounds.

How many elderly people were duped by the claims of the X corporation is not known. One imagines the number is considerable since major hearing loss is a terrible, socially incapacitating blow, especially to the aged.

A case history from the files of the New York League for the Hard of Hearing illustrates the misery which callous promoters can visit upon an older person:

For three years, Mrs. A. F., seventy-two, had carefully hoarded her change for the day when she might purchase a hearing aid. From her small pension check, she managed to take care of the rent for her tiny room, her small food bill, medical expenses, and the necessities of life. She managed to save $350 for an eyeglass hearing aid which, she thought, would bring her back into contact with people and destroy the barriers which isolated her from companionship.

Taking her cash in hand, she went to a hearing-aid dealer and purchased the aid that the salesman told her was right for her. To her surprise, she did not seem to be able to hear much better with the aid. She thought that in time she might become accustomed to it.

When several weeks went by and she found that the aid did not help her to hear better, she tried to contact the dealer for assistance. She thought that perhaps the instrument could be adjusted so that it would be useful.

Mrs. F. never succeeded in reaching the dealer.

Finally, Mrs. F. wrote to the manufacturer of the aid. The company responded by telling Mrs. F. that she had purchased her hearing aid from a dealer who had no authority to sell that device. As a result of her action in making the purchase from an unauthorized dealer, Mrs. F. had no legal protection. Her savings were dissipated for a useless hearing aid.

To avoid these problems, the U.S. Department of Health, Education and Welfare strongly urges these guidelines in selecting a hearing aid:

- Compare for clarity and quality of sound. Listen to familiar voices with each aid;
- Compare how well you understand with each aid—listen in noisy places as well as quiet—outdoors as well as indoors;
- Check the aid for comfort and convenience—controls should be easy to operate; batteries, parts, etc., should be available locally;
- Check the costs. A low-priced hearing aid may be satisfactory—depending on your needs;
- Look for the extra services. Do you get a money-back guarantee? Will the dealer help you to learn to use the aid?

8   Eyes and Glasses: Don't Do It Yourself

Frauds against the elderly in the field of eye care were the subject of two days of hearings before a subcommittee of the Senate Committee on Aging. One of the principal witnesses, the Chairman of the Federal Trade Commission—citing that body's "long and extensive experience with those who would prey on the many sufferers from failing eyesight"—gave examples of the various types of swindles.

There are those who peddle useless devices—accompanied by a course of instruction—which purport to offer treatment for eye defects without resort to glasses, drugs, or surgery.

These ads claim that a "new and revolutionary" system improves eyesight, eliminates headaches and nervousness, overcomes tired feelings, and causes the eyes to become clear and strong. In addition, by testing his eyes with the device, the user can "adjust" them, making each eye better able to see alone as well as in harmony with the other. Eventually glasses are discarded.

Eyeglasses sold through the mails also come under FTC surveillance. Many such offers fraudulently exaggerate the effectiveness of simple magnifying glasses. In point of fact, the FTC concluded that these glasses were capable of correcting defects in vision of persons approximately forty years of age and older who do not have astigmatism or diseases of the eye.

Other mail-order glasses operators claim to sell lenses ground "in accordance with prescriptions." Out of a sample of fifteen pairs of such glasses examined by the FTC, only five fulfilled that promise.

A classic example of out-and-out fraud in mail order eyeglasses involved widespread advertisements placed in newspapers and publications by a con man offering magnifying reading glasses at $3.95—satisfaction guaranteed. When victims returned the glasses, (actually valued at 25 cents) under the guarantee, the operator, doing business as Jenar Co., sent a postal card claiming a lens was broken, and the guarantee did not cover this situation. A three-month investigation disclosed that the swindler was, in many instances, actually mailing glasses with broken lenses, and had taken the public—mostly elderly people—for about $75,000.

Another gimmick is eyeglasses offered at greatly reduced prices, which the FTC found, were unsuited for the great majority of persons. The ads are used as bait to induce purchasers to visit stores, where they are examined and advised that their eyes are in such serious condition that they require much higher-priced glasses. Frequently the expensive glasses were no different from the originally advertised useless and harmful glasses.

Misrepresentation about sun glasses includes exaggeration of almost nonexistent reduction of glare and false claims that lenses are ground and polished.

In the contact-lens field, there have been bootleg outfits that sell cheap, but employ no qualified vision specialist to fit them. The result is a "bargain" that either can't be worn, or, if it is, can cause blindness or damage to the eyes. In addition, there have been widespread false claims that all persons in need of visual correctives can successfully wear contact lenses without the slightest discomfort or irritation.

False and misleading advertising in the eye-care field has been by no means limited to the promotion of eyeglasses and contact lenses.

In one instance, the FTC found that an advertiser claimed that a mineral-food supplement would restore sight to the blind and cure ulcer of the cornea, conjunctivitis, and glaucoma. Also, a drug preparation was represented as a cure for cataracts, cloudiness of vision, film carnosity, and inflammation of the eyes.

Another advertiser of a drug preparation was told to cease and desist from representing that it would be of any therapeutic value in the treatment of granulated eyelids.

There are numerous small groups, within the eye-care field, that adhere to highly questionable procedures. Although there is usually some possible scientific base for their theory or school of thought, the methods they advocate are considerably outside the mainstream of sound practice.

One such school of medical thought holds that sunlight, by its very nature, is harmful to the eyes and that the sure-fire method to prevent the formation of cataracts is the automatic prescribing of tinted lenses—particularly selective in absorbing the infra-red end of the spectrum—for everyone.

Another such dubious area is the indiscriminate use of diathermy, which is arbitrarily prescribed despite the fact that the patients' problems may range from cataract to glaucoma to conjunctivitis.

Of particular concern to the optometric profession is the school of thought called "syntonics." The basis of this theory lies in the treatment of various visual and eye problems with chromatic light of various colors (wave lengths) and intensities. A letter from the College of Syntonic Optometry explains:

"The application of the syntonic principle is not new. Reference has been made as to results obtained as early as 1,500 B.C., but it took many years of experimentation and coordinated thought for a genius, Dr. H. Riley Spitler, to assemble the known laws of physics, cytology, biology, physiology, neurology, and optometry into one applicable technique and present it to the profession interested in the improvement and preservation of human vision."

"It is the purpose of the College of Syntonic Optometry to carry on the work of Dr. Spitler as it applies to optometry. The fundamental lectures will be given to assembled classes of five or more by one of the instructors designated by the college. The lectures require several days, and upon their completion the applicant will be competent to apply syntonics to his patients with either too high or too low expected findings in his 'analytical examination,' and to get surprising results."

The over-the-counter sale of ready-made (so-called Grandma)

glasses also came in for scrutiny at the Senate hearing. This practice was characterized by an official of the American Optometric Association as "particularly pernicious" because:

They are used mostly by the ill-informed elderly.

The elderly are most prone to eye and general disease.

The use of ready-made eyeglasses may, by giving some improvement in vision, mask the underlying causes of changes in vision.

He went on to list the dangers of such self-prescription:

Changes in vision in the elderly may be symptomatic of eye conditions or bodily diseases, most of which would be disclosed by an eye examination, and many of which could be corrected if discovered and treated early.

Self-treatment through the use of ready-made eyeglasses causes delay that can make successful correction more difficult or impossible.

Ready-made eyeglasses never contain, and never could be made to contain, any correction of astigmatism, a condition prevalent in over 90 per cent of all eyes.

Most people's eyes are not optically identical. Ready-made eyeglasses must ignore this very significant fact, since the two lenses must be of equal power.

In New Jersey alone it is estimated that some 200,000 persons, forty years of age or older, use ready-made eyeglasses. These, and others across the nation, who practice self-prescription leave themselves exposed to undetected glaucoma, cataracts, diabetic retinopthy, and blinding, disabling, or fatal diseases.

Some operators of the mail-order glasses business have developed a sensitivity to charges that they are giving the same prescription for thousands whose defective vision varies greatly.

To counter this allegation they have developed a do-it-yourself test-your-own-eyes kit. One demonstrated before the Senate Subcommittee on Frauds and Misrepresentations Affecting the Elderly had gadgets that could measure the frame size, curvature of the ear piece, and fit the nose bridge. Of course, it also provided an eye chart and instructions for taking a "self-test-optometer."

The letter chart is placed ten feet away. There is a gadget with ten or twelve lenses in it. To test distance vision it is held to the eye to find the lens that allows the chart to be seen most clearly. The number of this lens is recorded on a form. The other eye is checked and recorded. That takes care of the distance element of the glasses. For reading glasses the test is a card that says: "Buy glasses by mail and save money. You are guaranteed perfect satisfaction or your money will be cheerfully refunded. Our glasses are guaranteed to be manufactured accurately."

The wheel is turned until that legend is clear with each eye, and upon recording those numbers the examination is complete.

In addition, the catalogue allows a choice of frame and the type of bifocal lens. If you specify that light hurts your eyes, you can have a tint in your lenses for an additional $3.

The representative of the American Optometric Association who demonstrated this device aptly labeled it as "playing Russian roulette with your vision." That description would also apply to anyone who trusts his eyes to other than a licensed optometrist, opthomologist, or oculist.

9

Dental Quacks:
A Twenty Million Dollar Harvest

The American Dental Association estimates that the annual bite by dental quacks is in excess of $20,000,000. Describing this situation as "a menace to dental public health," the ADA cites studies which show that the bogus operator has his "greatest impact on the aged."

One ADA survey revealed 78.3 per cent of Americans past the age of sixty wear dentures or bridges and nearly two-thirds of those over sixty-five have either a complete upper or lower denture. Since these are the areas of dentistry in which the quack usually operates, it is obvious that the aged are his prime targets.

The injurious aspects of dealing with an unlicensed and unqualified peddler go beyond monetary waste. Ill-fitting and painful dentures make it impossible for the wearer to chew or consume many beneficial foods, and general deterioration of health may result.

The ADA warns that only a licensed dentist is qualified by professional training to diagnose dental conditions and determine the design of a dental prosthesis. Furthermore, all states have laws which permit only dentists or (in some cases) dental hygienists to work on a patient's mouth.

In spite of this, many of the aged fall victim to the unlicensed quack who promises fast service, perfect fit, and cheap prices because the "middle man"—the dentist—is eliminated.

In another ADA survey 9.4 per cent of people over the age of sixty indicated that they would consider going to a dental quack for dentures. If they did, the survey showed, they wouldn't even be saving much money, since the average cost of dentures received from dentists was only about $25 more than those obtained from quacks. But there is a world of difference in health service rendered.

The first step in planning a denture is correct diagnosis. The dentist must determine, by visual and Xray examination, the condition of the soft tissue and of the bone which must support the denture. He must examine the jaw joint and determine the various relationships that the denture should maintain. The dentist is aware of the many changes in the mouth that result from wearing dentures and from the aging process itself. Ill-fitting dentures can even give rise to oral cancer. Obviously, the dental quack has neither the education nor the inclination to understand and act upon such considerations.

Another dental racket is the home denture reliner and repair kit.

Many drugstores throughout the United States sell these kits which encourage the user to repair, reline, and adjust his own denture. They are sold with the promise that they will give the denture a better "fit."

This kit usually consists of impregnated paper or some sufficiently plastic material that can be adapted to the contour of both the dentures and the gums and ridges. These products and procedures are hazardous because the patient continues to wear an ill-fitting denture that endangers his dental and general health. They are sold on the basis of advertising and labelling that make promises that are never kept.

The following are typical of the national advertisements for these do-it-yourself kits:

"False teeth break? Good news! Now you can repair them at home in ten minutes."

"Broken or loose false plates? Fix it yourself easily in a few minutes. Your plates may become broken or loose just when you need them most. With Fix-It-Kit you can repair your own broken plates. Also tightens loose-fitting plates easily. Get permanent comfort with professional material. Complete instructions. Satisfaction guaranteed or your money refunded."

"Dental plates broken? Fix it yourself! Why wait days for repairs? Do it yourself in minutes. Save $5 to $10 on repairs by doing it yourself easily and inexpensively with this exciting 'denture repair kit.' Guaranteed to fix breaks, cracks and loose teeth. Keep 'denture repair kit' on hand for emergencies."

Every dentist knows that it is not uncommon to see patients whose residual ridges have been destroyed by ill-fiitting dentures. This condition is frequently seen in the mouths of patients who have relined or otherwise altered the shape of the impression surfaces on their own dentures with the so-called perfect-fit materials described above. When a patient attempts to change the shape of the impression surfaces of his dentures to improve the fit, the resulting stresses may cause excessive pressures on the underlying tissues. The final result is irreparable damage to the denture foundation.

Since dental quackery is a growing menace, the ADA is seeking to educate the public to its dangers. To this end it has produced a film, *Report on Bootleg Dentistry*, which is made available without charge to civic, fraternal, or educational groups.

10 Quackery Around the World:
Gullible's Travels

- A Filipino sleight-of-hand artist who performs "psychic surgery."
- A Rumanian doctor with a "rejuvenation cure" for the elderly.
- A Swiss clinic which offers "cellular therapy" for worn-out organs.
- The Tijuana "doctors" who cure every disease under the Mexican sun.

These are but a few of the foreign quacks who are making a fast buck by "treating" gullible elderly Americans.

Perhaps one of the most inexplicable—certainly the most bizarre—phenomenon in recent years is the planeloads of Americans flying to the Philippines to be ministered to by "psychic surgery." The leading "surgeon" in this field is Antonio Agpaoa, or "Doctor Tony" as he calls himself.

Eschewing any college of surgeons, "Dr. Tony" left school in the third grade and served his internship on the stage where he was a magician and sleight-of-hand artist. Somewhere along the line, he discovered that he could do abdominal, heart, and even brain surgery with his *bare hands,* without benefit of anesthesia. Furthermore, he found that he could close these purported "openings" without leaving a trace of the operation—no scar.

With such talent, Tony soon found American promoters who arranged public meetings at hotels and even churches in this country. The lectures consisted of movies of the "method" and testimonials from believers.

Tony must have been a great prestidigitator. Level-headed viewers of his film were convinced that he was making an incision into the abdomen with only his fingers and removing tumors and other diseased tissue. His boosters included chiropractors, naprapaths, and some clergymen. Tony's business boomed.

Today there are at least forty more "psychic surgeons" operating in the Philippines.

A little closer to home, there are the "cures" that can be had in Tijuana, Mexico, which is probably the quack capital of the Western Hemisphere, if not the world. Americans by the thousands cross the border for treatment of cancer, arthritis, etc.

There is, in fact, a group called the International Association of Cancer Victims and Friends with headquarters in San Diego, which has organized sponsorship drives for some Tijuana "cures." Their membership is currently reported at about 3,000. They publish a bi-weekly magazine and they steer people to the purveyors of worthless cures.

The "Laetrile" cancer cure (see pps. 79-80) is currently being offered in Tijuana by Ernesto Contreras, a pathologist. Also in business is a nurse who once worked at the Hoxey Cancer Clinic in Dallas, (see p. 76) and is now offering the Hoxey Treatment for cancer (outlawed in the United States). Her medicine consists of four ounces of cascara sagrada and potassium iodine mixed with a gallon of water. Sold in pint bottles, one gallon of this stuff nets the promoters $800.

Another Tijuana specialist dispenses Dr. Robert Liefman's drug, "Liefcort" (outlawed in the United States) for arthritis sufferers.

Also located along our southern border are a brother team of doctors at Mexicali, who have a treatment for arthritis based on steroid preparations. In addition, there is a Mexican physician at Piedras Negras; across the border from Eagle Pass, Texas, who utilizes the drug dipyrone for the treatment of arthritics. At least six persons are known to have died after taking dipyrone.

Mexico, especially Mexico City, has also developed a burgeoning school system which offers medical degrees for drug healers, such as chiropractors and naturopaths.

European healers, specializing in "rejuvenators" and revitalization of "worn-out" organs of the body, are particularly attractive to the well-heeled elderly.

For example, Ana Aslan, a Rumanian doctor, claims that old people have been helped to feel younger by injections of procaine and vitamins, which she calls "H-3." The majority of informed medical opinion sees little value in such use of procaine—better known as novocain. As Dr. Nathan Shock of the National Institute of Health put it: "If these claims for procaine were true, you'd be adding ten years to your life every time the dentist filled a tooth. This woman (Dr. Aslan) is the Pied Piper of the 60's, leading the aged instead of the young."

Professor Paul Niehans and others in Switzerland and Germany attract elderly Americans with claims for the benefits from "cellular therapy." They assert that the injections of embryonic cells from various organs of freshly killed animals will revitalize corresponding damaged or "worn-out" organs in man. There is no scientific evidence that this treatment has any value. In fact, according to Dr. Gerald D. Dorman, President of the American Medical Association, injection of foreign protein may cause a reaction in the recipient that can be harmful.

In England, authorities are concerned over the spread of "Scientology," which was originated by L. Ron Hubbard, an American science-fiction writer, who now lives in the United Kingdom.

The practitioners, or "auditors," of Scientology go through a course of orientation or training presumably to man outposts in what they now call the "Church of Scientology." In earlier years, the activity was known as "Dianetics."

In this country, the Food and Drug Administration during the past year obtained a federal court order upholding seizure of a large number of so-called "Hubbard E. Meters." This device, utilized as a diagnostic tool by the Scientology "auditors," was held as misbranded within the meaning of the federal law.

In an address before the Fourth National Congress on Health Quackery, sponsored by the AMA and the National Health Council in Chicago in October, 1968, AMA President Dr. Gerald D. Dorman saw international quackery as a growing threat to Americans and suggested some remedies:

"What really is needed is an educational campaign. This would not necessarily serve only to warn Americans against quackery in foreign countries. It would utilize communications media efficiently to emphasize medical facts. It would stress, among other things, that: (1) the best health care on this earth is available right here in the United States, if a disease is amenable to therapeutic measures that have been tested and evaluated in laboratories, hospitals and clinics by competent investigators, and (2) that it is neither necessary nor advisable for sick persons and their families to waste money and valuable time in search of a medical or surgical panacea beyond our borders.

"We should seek better ways to acquaint the American public with the accomplishments of medicine, particularly in the area of preventive medicine."

11 | Nursing Homes: Waiting for Death

"A State inspector reported finding that a particular home, having served a light supper at 4 P. M. made no provision for breakfast for its forty patients, about twenty of whom were bedfast, and almost all of whom were public-assistance recipients. Your money paid for all these unserved meals; and there is evidence that such poor care is all too commonplace."

This is an excerpt from lengthy testimony by Mrs. Mary Adelaide Mendelson, Associate Executive Secretary, Welfare Federation of Cleveland, before a 1967 session of the House Ways and Means Committee. Her picture of abuses by nursing homes in the Cleveland area was yet another in the shocking revelations which had earlier been aired at hearings of the Senate Aging Committee (Subcommittee on Long-Term Care) held in Indianapolis, Cleveland, Los Angeles, Denver, New York City, Boston, and Portland, Maine.

The investigations of nursing-home conditions in many parts of this country resulted in passage of legislation intended to elevate standards and strengthen State control of nursing home operators and operations as part of the Social Security Amendments of 1967 (see Appendix, p. 235).

The major abuses uncovered by the Senate were:

- Nursing homes were operating while continuously in violation of State licensure laws.
- Drugs were being prescribed and purchased for patients who never received them.
- Patients were entering nursing homes and staying there months and years without a re-evaluation of their condition.
- In some instances the apparent owners of nursing homes are not in fact the true owners, making code of enforcement difficult.
- Some nursing-home operators, victims of unscrupulous moneylenders, reduce services to patients in order to meet large debt payments and exorbitant interest rates.
- Many public-assistance patients were being maintained in homes that are unsafe and endanger their lives.

Mrs. Mendelson's testimony, which was described by the Senate Aging Committee as "the most detailed available account of nursing home abuses in any one city" reads in part:

[145

"Our study revealed that some physicians who were billing the State for two visits a month for old-age assistance patients in the nursing homes were not always seeing these patients two times a month. Bills rendered were for services not provided. In fact, one of the problems that we frequently hear decried is the difficulty of getting medical care for private patients in skilled nursing homes.

"Such, however, does not seem to be the case with public assistance patients, many of whom were presumably seen more times than the State licensing regulations required or the physical health of the patient necessitated—at least bills to the State would so indicate.

"Was the care actually provided? If it was, why are these patients frequently reported by the hospitals or the morgues as being emaciated, covered with bed sores, and physically neglected? Yet not once has a physician in my county called the Aid for Aged office to complain about the care provided by the home later criticized by other authorities.

"As a further example of possible fraud, I am reminded of payments made under the medical assistance program to a doctor for alleged medical care furnished a number of patients. This 'physician,' however, is neither listed in the telephone directories as a physician nor registered with the Academy of Medicine.

"Another curious fact, found in some instances, was that drugstores were being paid for 'furnishing' more drugs than the patients, or the nurses, or the nurses' records indicate were received.

"To what extent this is prevalent, I am in no position to say. However, it is a fact that one drugstore in my community annually does a $270,000 business in old age assistance drugs alone. There is no reason, in my judgment to assume that these medications were all actually delivered, and if delivered, used, and if used, needed. Indeed, one nursing home administrator has claimed that his particular home, as well as others, normally obtains his household supplies under the guise of drugs for patients, paid for as drugs by old age assistance. Another nursing home operator explained to me, and to the veterans hospital social worker, that his drugstore had billed a private patient three times in 1 month, to the amount of around $60 without ever itemizing the bill. The patient disclaimed having received that amount of medicine.

"One pharmacist has admitted that several nursing homes offered percentage kickbacks if he would service their telephone accounts. It was made clear that if the prescription is not for an unreasonable quantity, there would be no check by the authorities; and there was no way of knowing that the patient allegedly receiving the drugs either sees them or needs them.

"There are many other opportunities for supplementing nursing home 'income' through drug payments. For example, one of my informers has advised that a drugstore in my county popular with nursing homes is owned in substantial part by a nursing home operator managing a large number of beds.

"There are still other areas requiring inquiry: lab work that may not be needed, but is paid for public funds; podiatrists—with a frequency not generally countenanced in well-run homes—providing quick and routine toenail care, paid for by title (public funds) payments received for orthopedic shoes when the 'patient' is seen wearing only slippers; and so on.

"... another kind of theft is personal expense money, for example, which patients are supposed to get but never receive, clothes which are stolen, billings for beauty salon work that is never done, or social security checks which are never received."

A survey of county homes in Indianapolis revealed some other shocking aspects of the care and facilities provided for the aged.

- Fifty per cent of the buildings erected more than sixty years ago are still in operation—with but minor alterations. Most of these homes are obsolete and hazardous.
- Many homes do not require a medical examination on admission, do not provide a regular medical examination of their patients and, in fact, have no established policy of medical procedure.
- Although 20 per cent of the residents of county homes and twelve percent in nursing homes could be returned to their communities by a program of rehabilitation, such services are practically nonexistent.

Commenting on this report and on the general attitude of the medical profession toward the care of the elderly, Dr. Nathan Salon of the Indiana Commission on Aging and Aged, told the Senate Subcommittee on Long Term Care:

> "Many physicians are not interested in this facet of practice and therefore are not knowledgeable in the physical and mental aspects of aging. Our medical schools, except for a very few, offer no courses in geriatrics and the student and resident staffs of hospitals are not exposed to the medical aspects and to the psychodynamics of older people."

Dr. Salon called for a massive effort to reverse this situation:

> "The care of the disabled older person has become

the primary responsibility of every physician, every nurse, every social worker and the entire community.... Our sincere interest in the welfare of our patients, and our desire to provide the best possible service is most important. We are dealing with human beings, and this fact makes it imperative that we accept the social responsibility which our work entails."

Thomas G. Karsell, a reporter for the *Indianapolis Star,* who wrote a series of articles on nursing homes and care of the aged, told the Subcommittee of life inside these institutions:

"Outside of the church-sponsored or eleemosynary institution sponsored nursing home, or some of the very plush nursing homes, I have never seen any indication of any recreational program whatsoever.

"Most of the people either just stay in bed or sit against the wall. It is a pretty appalling sight.... Most of these people are simply waiting to die....

"If you have ever been in most of these places, you are immediately overwhelmed with the odor of cooked beans. I am not sure they serve anything else in these places....

"I can think of many places where there were no individual towels and washcloths. I have seen many places where the bed sheeting was just abysmally filthy."

Sentenced to a painful and undignified "wait for death" within these homes, the elderly are under constant threat of a quicker road to the grave. Statistics show that six patients die in nursing-home fires for every one killed in a hospital fire. Nursing homes are, in fact, the most prolific killers of institutional occupants due to fire.

An official of the National Fire Protection Association told a convention of the American Nursing Home Association of the need for more modern fire safety methods in nursing homes:

> "We have learned that the early solutions of alarms, attendants and evacuations are unsatisfactory in the light of present-day nursing-home fires. We have reviewed certain nursing home fires which caused a change in fire protection thinking. We have reviewed the normal development of fire and the speed of this development....
>
> "Through this study we have learned that the only implement for nursing homes presently at our disposal that will cut fire growth at the critical stage; that will block the generation of dangerous quantities of heat; that will chop the development of thick, choking smoke; that will provide time to move patients, if moving patients is necessary—the only implement is the complete automatic sprinkler system.
>
> "Without a complete automatic sprinkler system all our efforts at strict control of combustibles, severe limitation of interior finish, intensive staff training, practical evacuation plans, all our efforts will continue to fail as they have in the past. The unnecessary life loss from nursing homes will continue.
>
> "By 1985 there will be over 25 million potential patients. The flood of elderly has created a growing need for a fire-free, safe environment for these people.
>
> "We have learned from fire deaths that sprinklers in nursing homes are vital. Will we give heed to this clear lesson or will these dead have died in vain."

Senator Frank E. Moss of Utah, Chairman of the Subcommittee on Long-Term Care, called for a clause in the 1967

Social Security Amendments Bill that would pay nursing homes serving federally subsidized patients on the basis of "reasonable cost" rather than a flat fee. He summed up the Subcommittee's strong condemnation of many areas of nursing home operation:

"... Hearings and studies conducted by the Subcommittee on Long-Term Care of the Special Committee on Aging... showed that deplorable conditions exist in some nursing homes. In many cases patients who are presumably getting skilled nursing home care under our medical assistance programs are actually receiving no more than custodial care. Our public-assistance programs are maintaining many patients in homes that are unsafe and endanger their very lives. State licensing and inspection are not as effective as they should be in assuring safety and adequate care."

"... Public assistance payments are the economic backbone of the nursing-home industry. Sixty per cent of all patients in nursing homes are paid for by public assistance, and many homes have virtually all public assistance patients. We are currently paying a total of about $600 million per year for the care of these patients. The Department of Health, Education and Welfare tells us that if we pay the actual cost of care we will be paying $400 million more. In other words, the Department is telling us that we are meeting only 60 per cent of the cost involved in taking care of these patients. This seems incredible.

"If it is true that we are falling this far short of meeting our obligations under laws we have enacted, if it is true that we are imposing on providers of service and imposing on private paying patients to absorb 40 per cent of the burden of a public program, then I say it is a shame and we should put a stop to it forthwith.

But I don't believe it is true.... We have only to look about us at a thriving industry to see that it is not. No business would survive if it discounted the price of its product to 40 per cent below cost for a majority of its customers. Yet nursing homes are surviving. The many homes which have 80 and 90 per cent of their patients on welfare rates are not going out of business; indeed, they are expanding and building new facilities.

"... While the conscientious nursing-home administrator may be underpaid for his services, there is ample evidence that we are overpaying others in terms of value actually received and in some cases paying for goods and services not delivered at all.

"The findings of my subcommittee suggest that in some cases nursing home profits, for example, are extraordinary. At our hearing in Boston, a witness who had directed a study by the State legislature in Massachusetts told us '... we were satisfied that the nursing homes figured at least $1,000 a year profit per bed and that was on the basis of (welfare rates).' "

"This statement was disputed, of course, but its creditability is supported by reports from other states. A survey in another state reported an annual profit of over $1,000 per bed in a home where blind patients were sometimes served scrapings from plates of others. From another state we heard from an authoritative source of a 28-bed home which realized a profit of $32,000 and another of similar size which realized $44,000. In still another state in another region of the country, a local investigator was shown plans for a new home and was told by the owner that he expected to recover the entire construction cost in three years."

"... All of these homes have welfare patients. Our public assistance programs are paying a considerable part of these outrageous and unwarranted profits. Of course, a nursing-home owner expects to realize a return on his investment. This is entirely proper, but we cannot continue to countenance these kinds of profits squeezed out of public funds at the expense of helpless patients.

"Nursing-home financing provides in some cases another rathole into which we are pouring public money. My subcommittee learned of a case in which a nursing-home owner borrowed $1,300,000. That is, he executed a note for that amount but actually received $700,000. Thus it cost him $600,000 to obtain his capital, and public assistance funds paid a large share.

"... Public funds are paying these exorbitant financing costs while the care we are supposed to be reimbursing must be curtailed in order for the owner to meet his payments.

"... Are we paying for goods and services not delivered? We almost surely are.

"... Public assistance funds, both state and federal, are pouring through these cracks in the system. Total public assistance expenditures for nursing-home care exceed $600 million annually. How much of these funds is lost through unwarranted payments or even fraudulent payments? How much could be saved by a system of reimbursement based on the reasonable costs of services actually rendered; a system under which claims for payment are supported by appropriate records and accounting information which can be verified and audited? I do not know the answers to these questions... but I suspect the amounts are substantial.

"... I wish to make absolutely clear that in citing these abuses I am not attacking nursing homes in general. I will not recite the usual caveat that these conditions are true only of a small minority because it is my impression that they are far more prevalent than this kind of statement implies. But it is clear

to me that the present leadership of the industry
reflects a solid constituency of reputable businessmen
who deplore this exploitation of people and of the
public purse as much as anyone."

This strong polemic was underscored by two letters received
by the Subcommittee on Long-Term Care and made a part of
its records. The first was from a Cleveland man, whose mother
suffered a broken hip, who told of his experiences in trying
to get a bed in a nursing home for her during a two-month
period.

Nursing Home No. 1: "At that home two colored pratical
nurses showed affiant two vacant beds, and was told to contact
the registered nurse the next day before 6 P.M. Affiant went
there the next day—but nurse left at 5 P.M. instead of 6 P.M.
Affiant called the practical nurse by phone same evening;
nurse told him that the two beds were taken the day before."

No. 2: "Practical nurse showed affiant an empty bed—in
my presence the practical nurse talked to the owner about
my mother being a state case . . . the owner stated she could
not accept state case."

No. 3: "I was told that I could get a room if I would pay
the difference between the amount paid by the state ($175)
and the price of a private patient (about $300.)"

No. 4: "They said the state does not pay enough."

No. 5: "Owner would accept state case . . . but the home
is too congested."

No. 6: "Said they put my mother's case on the waiting
list. I did not see the list to see how many were ahead of my
mother."

No. 7: "A modern nursing-home manager stated they were

a private home and did not have to take state cases."

No. 8: "I was told by the Chronic Illness Center to visit several homes—the implication being that there were some vacancies there—but on arrival I was told there are no vacancies . . . (after I mentioned that the patient was a state-supported case)."

The second document was a profoundly moving letter from a Colorado woman, who had been forced to put her mother in a nursing home.

"After much deliberation and deep concern for conditions existing in private nursing homes I feel I must speak out and make what I have observed known.

"Due to circumstances beyond my control, it is necessary to have my mother in a local nursing home. Visiting her every other day for a period of 14 months I observe things the casual visitor does not note. The comments I am about to make are directed to private nursing homes. Those with county or church affiliations are vastly better managed nursing homes.

"Just what is a first-class nursing home? Are they places designed to rehabilitate and/or help the aged to retain active interest in themselves and their surroundings or are they places where there is nothing left but to resign oneself and vegetate?

"Many of the elderly are not yet ready to sit and stare at four walls or sit and nap much of the time. A sweet and very articulate little old lady made this remark: 'When you know there is nothing you can do about the situation you are in you must resign yourself to accepting the conditions that exist or lose your mind.' How right she is.

"In the home in which my mother is staying there is

no person to give occupational therapy or to direct simple recreational activities. Three walls of the lounge are lined with comfortable chairs and a TV in one corner which must be viewed from a distance too great for most to be able to see the screen with clarity.

"There is no person to give even the most rudimentary physical therapy. At the time mother was admitted, members of the family provided simple manipulative toys recommended by a hospital therapist. We went to the home and personally helped her go through the exercises. Some months back, when the manager feared an investigation because he had no therapist, he hired a woman who is not a registered therapist but who has had illness in her family which necessitated learning to give simple therapy. Mother showed much response and was regaining the use of an arm and leg paralyzed from a stroke. She has a great deal of fight and we were all so pleased that she was winning her battle. What did the manager do? At what seemed a crucial point in Mom's recovery he told the woman he no longer needed a therapist. Unless I walk my mother she does not get walked. At the present time there is much leg swelling and she must wear elastic bandages. Our doctor says this is the direct result of not being walked. Another person in town, who has no means of transportation, hires a taxi to take her well beyond the city limits each day so that she may walk her father and shave him. Without her love and devotion the old gentleman would simply vegetate. Just what are we, or the state, paying for in the way of care?

"There is a staff shortage but the place is very poorly managed. How can a manager know the needs of his institution when he keeps himself closed in his office, with his graphs and copies of the *Wall Street Journal,* day in and day out? As I see it, he deliberately keeps the place understaffed. It is cheaper that way. He constantly laments that he cannot make it on the amount he receives from the patients.

"I have few complaints to make about the nurses' aids. They work long hours and are underpaid. These women must have much compassion for the elderly infirm or they could not stand it. They have time only for routine things. Their hands are tied by the facilities available and the management.

"It is true that stealing is a common practice. I assume the temptation is great. However, they know the management has one sign a release from responsibility in case of fire, theft, or accidents. This, I feel, contributes to a laxity on the part of both management and the help. Incidentally, there is proof of padding of bills for medication in a Denver nursing home. We have no way of knowing how much such bills should be. Some doctors feel that prescriptions are renewed too often. It is understandable that there is a feeling of distrust of both personnel and management of nursing homes in general.

"Food is often so very poor. Being a graduate home economist I can verify that the particular home of which I speak serves food poor beyond belief—yet occasionally serves very good meals. A Sunday-evening meal served to my mother two weeks ago consisted of a small serving of stale peach slices, a portion of canned tomatoes, mostly juice, half a grapefruit cut in such a way that the segments were hard to separate, a back from a fried chicken which was left from a previous meal, and a small handful of potato chips. Many persons have suffered strokes and it is most difficult to eat such foods with one hand. The combination of foods was nauseating.

"I quarrel with the management over the food and the manner in which it is served, as my mother is a diabetic. The manager asked if I would prepare menus for him as he admitted having trouble with the diabetics. I complied and prepared menus for a period of two weeks. I knew in my heart they would never be used. Most of the cooks are women from the neighborhood who know nothing of therapeutic diets. Often the manager's wife prepares the menus. They are designed to be as cheap as possible regardless of the patient's needs....

"Somewhere along the line there is not enough enforcement of standards, both physical and mental. All too many homes are being operated to fatten the pocketbooks of the managers to the detriment of the elderly. I dislike too much government control but there is a need for pressure being brought to bear on these homes. Inspections need to be made without any previous warning of any kind. Otherwise, for a brief time, conditions are improved just as they are on Mondays when the doctors are due to call.

"The public needs to be educated as to what services and care one should be getting from homes of various classifications. Those of us who have loved ones in these homes need this information. Perhaps we could put a little pressure on these places ourselves and help to see that standards are upheld."

12 | Health Insurance:
Cheap is Often Worthless

An elderly man or woman covered by adequate health insurance is far less likely to fall into hands of the quack or charlatan. Unfortunately for many aged people this safeguard is hard to come by.

The plight of the elderly in securing adequate health insurance is a bleak one. Private health insurance is unable to provide the large majority of the 19 million older Americans with hospital protection at premium costs they can afford. Approximately only half hold hospital insurance policies of any kind. Many others—predominantly the very old, those in poor health, the unemployed, and those with the lowest incomes—are without hospital insurance.

In addition, the elderly who now hold private insurance, are having difficulty keeping even an adequate level of protection. They find themselves squeezed between higher premiums and shrinking benefits, as hospital and medical costs continue to climb.

As a result, increasing numbers of older people are confronted with financial catastrophe should illness strike.

All this provides a mass market for the swindler who peddles "cheap" health insurance. More often than not "cheap" translates to worthless. This is borne out by one of the major findings of the Senate Subcommittee on Frauds and Misrepresentations Affecting the Elderly:

Economic pressures on older Americans are causing many to turn to mail-order health insurance offered by marginal companies which distort or omit facts in order to suggest that the policy gives more protection than it really does.

Direct-mail insurers issue about $45 million a year to policy holders who pay comparatively small monthly premiums against financial and personal tragedy at time of great need. Such protection, unfortunately, frequently exists in the mind of the purchaser and not in the print of the policy. At the Subcommittee hearing a representative of the Federal Trade Commission stated that complaints and investigation of misrepresentations and frauds have jumped dramatically in recent years. He detailed the most common forms of word hocus-pocus now in use.

Misrepresentation of Policy Termination Provisions

The claims

"No automatic termination age—total disability for accident or confining sickness is paid at the rate of one-half the regular monthly benefit for life if incurred after age sixty."

"No reduction in benefits because of age."

"Benefits do not decrease at any age."

"You and your family are covered from 1 to 75."

The facts

Most of the policies sold in this field are renewable solely at the option of the company. Each new premium purchases insurance for a new term. The majority of these policies can be canceled by the company at the end of any term for any reason. This is done by refusing to accept the premium payment.

Misrepresentation of Extent of Coverage

The claims

"Accident benefits include $50 weekly payable from the first day of total disability every thirty days for as many as 104 weeks for *each* mishap . . . $25 weekly for as many as 26 weeks for partial disability . . . as much as $5,200 for each accident, with no reduction on account of other insurance."

The facts

There are many cases of accident or sickness for which these policies do not provide payment. For example, many will not pay at all for losses due to certain causes such as nervous disorders, dental operations, venereal disease, etc.; they will not pay for losses due to other causes such as hernia, tuberculosis, heart disease, appendicitis, etc., unless originating at least six months after the policy date; and they will not pay for any loss due to sickness which can be traceable to conditions existing prior to the date of the policy.

MISREPRESENTATION OF MAXIMUM DOLLAR LIMITS

The claims

"Surgery from $3 to $150 depending on seriousness of operation."

"We pay up to $525 for each surgical operation."

"Surgical fees, up to $400."

The facts

These imply that if a person has a surgical operation, he will receive up to the amount specified, depending on the cost of the operation. Actually, many policies provide that the full amount is payable only for one or two comparatively rare operations. The maximum amount payable for the average operation is one-fourth of the specified amount, or even less.

MISREPRESENTATION OF BEGINNING TIME OF COVERAGE

The claims

"Benefits from the first day."

"Pays from the first day of medical attention."

"Monthly lifetime income is paid from the first day of disability."

"Full benefits payable from the very first day of disability and medical attention."

"Accidental benefits in effect the same day policy issued."

"A new plan that pays you a large monthly income from the first day you are disabled at home."

The facts

Indemnification is not provided from the first day of sickness or accidental injury; on the contrary, the policies provide that indemnification will be provided only for sickness originating more than thirty days after the policy date. Diseases of organs not common to both sexes, and diseases of the heart or circulatory system, are not covered until the policy is in effect from six to twelve months.

MISREPRESENTATION CONCERNING HEALTH STATUS OF APPLICANT

The claims

"No red tape—you don't have to join a group or be examined."

"No physical examination needed."

The facts

This implies full coverage without regard to the general health of the applicant when the policy is issued. What the advertisements do not disclose is that the policy does not cover any loss traceable to a condition in existence at the time the policy was issued.

MISREPRESENTATION CONCERNING SALE OF A PLAN

The claims

"Here's what you get. Streamlined, all-family plan issued by old-line, legal-reserve stock company, lowers cost, cuts red tape, pays you promptly and pays you more. Up to:

"$1,800 for hospital room.

"$5,000 for loss of life.

"$500 for surgery fees.

"$200 per month when off work due to accidental or totally confining sicknesses.

"$115 for childbirth.

"$150 per year for doctor's calls in the home or hospital.

"All this wonderful coverage costs you less than most folks spend for smokes."

The facts

These companies imply that a great number of benefits can be obtained from the purchase of one policy for a few cents a day when actually three policies must be purchased to get all the benefits listed in the ad.

MISREPRESENTATION OF BENEFITS AS PAYABLE FOR LIFE

The claims

"What will it mean to you to have $100 a month for the rest of your life, if totally disabled by sickness or accident?

"Pays up to $100 per month income for the rest of your life . . . payable as long as you are disabled and cannot work because of any accident or any confining sickness."

The facts

Such payments are provided only for a limited period of time in cases of disability due to sickness or cases of partial disability due to accident. Only in cases of absolute total disability due solely to accidental bodily injury are the payments made as represented.

Because most avenues to the better commercial insurers are blocked to the elderly, they are most susceptible to these siren songs sweetly crooning "low cost, no exam, comprehensive hospital and medical coverage, no ifs, ands or buts, no limitations . . . all for pennies a day."

Another growing problem is the unprincipled insurance agent who does not record previous ailments on insurance contracts. In consequence, when sickness occurs, the policy is void because of pre-existing conditions. Invariably the agent has disappeared and the parent company is not liable. Sometimes "gangs" of such agents blanket a community for a fast hit-and-run buck. A former Insurance Commissioner for the State of Michigan explained this operation:

"They descend on areas with a high percentage of elderly people, and conveniently leave out past medical history in the application forms. In some instances they hear of past medical history from the elderly applicant. However, they do not put it into the application. In other instances they do not even bother to ask. They automatically write no, no, no, no, or they might say to somebody, 'Well, a little ulcer condition such as the one you are talking about has no bearing on our company's underwriting attitude.'"

An example of the tragedy wrought by this kind of fraud was described by an investigator for the State of California:

"We went to one home and here we found a retired couple. He was seventy-four years of age. He had been approached by an operator and was sold on dropping his Blue Cross—Blue Shield. He was convinced by this 'sharpie' that he was getting more for less.
"This man had a history of diabetes and had suffered a stroke. He told the agent of this past medical history. The new policy was still issued. Several months later, the insured had a leg amputated as a result of his diabetes condition. Within one month he had a second stroke. Bills from these two claims totalled over $3,500. Both claims were rejected by the X company. The reasons were twofold, pre-existing conditions and that he had withheld important medical information from

[165

the company. We called an officer of the company into our office. In the middle of our negotiations with this company to settle this claim, the insured passed away."

Another major finding of the Senate Subcommittee went to the heart of a problem which bothers concerned individuals in and out of the insurance game:

Wide opportunities for deception and confusion exist in sales of health insurance policies because buyers are usually dependent upon the good faith of the seller for accurate interpretation of provisions.

According to many experts who testified before the Committee, it takes too sophisticated a buyer of health benefits to overcome the purveyor's policy of *caveat emptor*. Others have harsher criticisms. One congressman put it this way: "The insurance and service plan trade associations in the health and accident field are destroying their industry by this policy of 'let the buyer beware.'"

13 | The Mail-Order Land Boom: A Bust?

Until recent years, comparatively few Americans dreamed of retiring in distant states on land they had never seen. The mail-order land-sale boom made many dream and buy.

To many individuals near or past retirement age, the bright advertising brochures seemed to offer solid reason to believe that security, good climate, and a new way of life could be found on faraway sites in communities not yet built. Soon, however, many law-enforcement officials began to find flaws in the boom and tried to alert would-be purchasers to overly optimistic promoters and outright swindlers.

[167

Newspaper want ad recruiting help for real estate sales schemes.

[168

This swamp was sold as a "sunny retirement haven" for retired persons.

Concerned about the potential impact of mail-order land sales on the elderly, the Senate Committee on Aging turned its attention to the industry during its 1963 hearings. This preliminary study and subsequent testimony before the Subcommittee on Frauds and Misrepresentations Affecting the Elderly rounded out a most unsavory picture.

The president of the Better Business Bureau told the Senators that millions of dollars have been, and are being, spent by the aging public to buy faraway lots, sight unseen. This includes land in British Honduras, Brazil, Costa Rica, Venezuela, the Bahamas, and Hawaii, as well as Southwestern United States and Florida. In Mojave County, Arizona, alone there are more than 300 subdivisions with hundreds more in New Mexico, California, Texas, Oregon, Florida, Idaho, and Utah.

Many homesites are purchasable on a $10 down, $10 monthly basis. These have a particular appeal to those on limited social security or retirement incomes.

High-pressure sales campaigns—including illustrated advertising matter grossly distorting the true nature of the land offered—are conducted in cities far distant from the developments. These have induced many old people to buy lots in remote, desolate areas, lacking in roads, utilities, neighbors, schools, stores or any other evidence of civilization. Deception results not only from misrepresentation, but from the failure of the promoter to disclose the real character of the land and its location.

Some of these lots offered are in the vast arid areas of the Southwest where water must be either trucked to the home like fuel oil at so much per gallon, or be pumped up through artesian wells sunk several hundred feet below the earth's surface at substantial expense. As one promoter admitted about the area he was developing, "You'd have to pioneer to live there now."

Some of these lots have far too much water. Swamp merchants in Florida have accumulated many hard-earned dollars from the elderly, touting land in or near the Everglades. For example, Cypress Swamp in Collier County is "America's Last Frontier" and "Today's Best Investment." These ads do not disclose that the land may be under water part or all of the year, that drainage of the area would necessitate a public undertaking, and that there are no plans for such a project now or in the foreseeable future. In fact, some of the area is in a water-conservation zone where it is government policy to maintain water as a barrier.

Following the hearings, Senate Subcommittee staff members made field trips to seven states. They found that although the harsh light of publicity has cut deeply into the more blatant forms of fraud—such as selling land the promoter does not own—there is a vast "gray" area of operation that manages to walk a shaky tightrope between legality and fraud.

The investigators concluded that the law is next to powerless against shrewdly constructed slippery language and omission of important facts which can cause almost total misunderstanding and confusion.

Here are some of those tricks:

Artists' conceptions are not labeled as such.

Alleged or suggested nearby—but actually quite distant—scenes are routinely used, instead of on-site or accurately labeled photos.

What pass to the uninformed as maps are too frequently prepared with shocking disregard to scale and proportion.

Recreational areas, bodies of water, and places where shopping, schools, and other facilities which might be available are pictured much closer than they are.

Distances tend to be indicated as "minutes away" instead of hours (at legal speeds) or in miles over travelable roads. To fulfill one calculation you would have to drive sixty-eight miles in forty-five minutes, which is a little beyond the driving capability of most people.

The fact that flash floods, windstorms, sandstorms, temperature extremes, and other weather phenomena affect some areas is not usually revealed; nor are such things as water depth (and cost to reach it) and the absence of vital services.

A matter of a firm declaration of exactly what improvements will be installed—and when—is usually omitted.

The usual money refund and transfer guarantees are far more useful to the promoter than to the investor. The ads lull one into thinking it must be safe, but on close scrutiny, the money is returnable only on inspection and often only at the property rather than at the point of sale.

The "guarantees' are sometimes amusing. One even makes the generous pledge that the "full acre rancho" embraces 43,560 square feet, which is a little like guaranteeing that a foot is twelve inches.

The contract clauses the developer wants read are in bold black, other less inviting clauses are on the reverse side of the document in pale gray. It often takes strong light, real diligence, and optimum visual acuity to penetrate that verbiage.

The tracts are sold in installment contracts with 5 or 6 per cent interest on the unpaid balance. No deed is recorded until the contract is paid off. Most contracts stipulate that the property reverts to the seller if the buyer misses one or two payments, and the seller is not required to notify the buyer that he is delinquent. Thus, many of these lots are sold over and over again, year after year, as buyers stop their monthly payments for any number of reasons—they die, come upon hard times, or come down and see the land.

Few promoters make any improvements in the land. Some will dig a small drainage ditch, and give it a high-sounding name such as "Grand Canal," or put in a road or two, and bulldoze the swamps that can be seen from the main road, if indeed there is a main road. This window-dressing enables the unscrupulous operator to tell his prospects that he is "improving" the property. Actually, if no real improvements are planned, he is required by the installment land sales board to say so in all of his advertising material, but these facts usually appear in the small print.

A fairly new trend in mail-order sales is recommending the land as an investment for resale later at a profit, or buying it now, so that when retirement age is reached, the land will be paid for and ready for occupancy.

Unlike those who claim that their acreage is idyllic and well endowed with modern conveniences, the investment merchandiser usually admits that his land is undeveloped and without any public facilities at all. He also suggests, however, that the value of the land is almost certain to go up, perhaps to two or three times the original investment. He will also probably point out that Miami Beach and Los Angeles once were regarded as poor investment risks, but that fortunes have been made from wise real estate purchases on land once regarded as absolutely unpromising.

One investigator told the Senate Subcommittee on Frauds and

Misrepresentations Affecting the Elderly, of a "search" for land sold for investment:

"I spent almost two days, using a slow plane and a four-wheel-drive radio-equipped jeep, to try to locate a certain parcel in a development called University Highlands, being sold by a corporation named First America Corp., located approximately ten miles west of Daytona Beach in a dismal swamp.

"After some of the roughest riding, we had to give up, as it was impossible to penetrate deep enough into the swamp to a point which we had spotted from the air."

Incidentally, this parcel was sold to a woman from Syracuse, New York, who had intended to use it as "a homesite for a trailer house."

A reporter told the Senators of his experience in Mojave County, Arizona: "When you top a mountain rise, you can see the entire valley. There is not a sign of human habitation, except every few miles there are signs saying, 'This is Shangri-La Rancheros' or 'Heavenly Acres.' Then you go into the county courthouse and ask the county clerk, 'Are people out there really buying that land?' And he laughs and shows you the deeds, with tens of thousands of names of people in New York, New Jersey, and Illinois, paying their $10 or $20 a month on that same land that you just walked off of."

Because mail and printed ads have recently come under stricter surveillance by Federal and state agencies, the telephone "boiler room" staffed by fast talking con men is now favored by many operators.

These companies subscribe to Wide-Area Telephone Service (WATS) which allows them to make unlimited numbers of long-distance calls at flat monthly rates. It costs $2,475 a month for one WATS telephone on which calls can be made to any place in the continental United States. This is a very expensive way to sell, but obviously it pays off.

For proportionately less money, the companies can get phones covering limited sections of the country. A telephone-company official estimated that there are least six such operations in the Miami area alone. The same official said their monthly phone bills would "knock your hat off."

One company has used as many as six WATS phones at one time, four nationwide and two limited. That means they spend somewhere around $14,000 a month for telephones alone.

The con-man employed in the "boiler room" sells on commission. A good one can make up to $25,000 a year. Total sales, then, must be well up in the millions of dollars.

As mail order land sales have become a multimillion-dollar business, the various states in which large-scale developments are located, or in which there is a heavy volume of mail order sales, have attempted to protect their citizens from fraudulent or misleading sales.

The most common regulatory technique is "full disclosure." Under this statute, the developer is required to submit detailed data as to the condition of the land he proposes to sell to the state real estate commission or department before he is permitted to sell within the state. Then, hopefully, the buyer will study the statistics and often cryptic language of a public report on land development with the same interest that he reads the glossy brochure of the salesman.

However, according to many experts, no new laws can prevent the serious consequences of mail-order land sales of the 1950's and 1960's which, they say, are yet to come. The effect of these sales has been described as a "built-in time bomb." Here's why:

Most of this land is being sold off on installment contracts, generally being paid off over nine or ten years. Since the boom only reached large-scale proportions relatively recently, these contracts won't begin to mature for a few years. When they do, thousands of elderly will arrive in worthless desert or swamp, their money and dreams of graceful retirement gone forever.

Even for those elderly who find their purchase "habitable," there will be other insurmountable problems in counties of the South and Southwest. As a councilman from Naples, Florida put it:

> "We have a beautiful, quiet little community. It has been growing well. Normally it would continue to grow gradually and, as it grew, commercial enterprises would come in to broaden the tax base, and the people coming in would produce tax revenue.
>
> "Now, suddenly, the population of the entire county will be doubled and tripled, and these new people will live in low-cost homes. Therefore, because of Florida's homestead exemption, under which the first $5,000 of the assessment on homes is tax-exempt, they will produce almost no new revenue for the county. Right now the county is extended right up to hilt to pay for the needs of the people who live here. Who is going to pay for the policing of the new development? The developer isn't. The garbage collection, the schools, the fire protection, any one of a dozen other things.
>
> "I foresee little clumps of houses out there—tar-paper shacks, trailers, and hundreds of people begging the

county to help them out. And the county can't possibly have the resources to do it."

Or as a representative of the Better Business Bureau observed:

"Without industries to provide them jobs to eke out their Social Security and pension checks, without adequate municipal services, hospitals or adequate funds for welfare, what is to become of them?"

14

Buying A Funeral:
Swindlers Beyond the Grave

The 1964 hearings before the Senate Subcommittee on Frauds and Misrepresentations Affecting the Elderly spent several sessions looking into the practices of funeral service gyp artists operating in the pre-need burial field.

Most experts agree that it is good planning to pay for a burial in advance. It offers the opportunity to select the type of funeral at the price one wants to pay, rather than leaving these decisions to survivors, who must make the decisions while their minds are clouded by grief.

However, as a Better Business Bureau pamphlet, *The Pre-*

arrangement and Prefinancing of Funerals warns: "In recent years a growing number of individual firms and groups have sought to stimulate public interest in prearranged, prefinanced funeral plans. Grievous disappointments and severe financial losses have resulted from some unsound promotional schemes, foisted on a credulous public by armies of high-pressure salesmen..."

Today, well-organized sales campaigns for prepaid burial service plans—some using IBM cards for mail payments or even telephone "boiler room" tactics—are common.

These operators promise far more than is actually provided in the contract terms. The dangers of fraud inherent in this field were clearly stated in a decision of the Supreme Court of Illinois:

"In the long interval between full receipt of the purchase price and contract performance, the opportunities for fraud are great and the risk of insolvency, with consequent inability to perform, apparent."

Unfortunately, these dire predictions have often become fact throughout our nation. Sales are in the millions of dollars and contract purchasers—many elderly—find they cannot get what they thought they had paid for.

A typical example was recounted to the Senators by a representative of the Attorney General's office of New Mexico. The firm selling the pre-need service operates out of Colorado. Nevertheless the sales in New Mexico are made door to door and are on the installment basis. The purchaser signs a promissory note, is given a packet of IBM cards and envelopes, and is requested to mail his payments directly to Denver.

Once the funds leave New Mexico, that state's authorities can offer only minimum protection and have no concrete knowledge of how the funds are disposed. Investigation has uncovered only minimal assets in New Mexico.

The group's written contracts purport only to furnish caskets. The contract's total purchase price is usually $637.50 per plan, or what professional statistics show is approximately the regional average for complete funeral services, including the casket.

Purchasers naturally believe that these so-called casket contracts include complete funeral services.

The actual cost of the casket alone is $96.50. Thus, fooled by tricky language, the elderly buy items worth $96.50 for $637.50.

Also prevalent are fraudulent claims that contracts will guarantee "complete funeral services anywhere in the United States or Canada."

Typical is the case of one family who entered into two contracts for $1,325 each—payable $29 monthly—upon the express representation that the services covered could be performed by the funeral home of the family's choice.

After becoming suspicious six months and $145 in payments later, the family inquired whether the benefits would be, in fact available at the funeral establishment of their preference. They were told that another funeral home, not of their choice, would be used at contract price. For the family to use the establishment of their choice would cost $500 in additional payments. This was in direct contradiction to the message of the firm's newspaper advertising and the spiel of the salesman.

In truth, however, at the time the plans were sold, this company had contracts with only three funeral homes in the state.

15 Social Security Benefits: The Impostor Game

Given the meager sums of Social Security payments, one would guess that this area would not attract the wolfpack that feed on the aged. It would be a wrong guess. A variety of schemes have been devised to separate aged beneficiaries from the checks which, in many cases, are their main source of support.

High on the list is the con man who impersonates a Social Security employee to gain access to the beneficiary's home and confidence. Once this relationship is established, there are a variety of dodges used. Here are a few, along with actual case histories from the files of the Social Security Administration.

1. A promise of either a bonus or increased monthly benefits, after payment of a set fee to the impostor.

Case History: A confidence man in Piqua, Ohio, contacted a Social Security beneficiary and told him his monthly benefit was low because he had one year's low earnings. He advised the beneficiary that for a fee of $98 he could get him a lump-sum payment of $3000.

The beneficiary was willing, but the confidence man said that since he had no blanks, he would return Saturday, which he did. The victim gave him his check for that amount. Fortunately, in this case, the victim visited a Social Security office the next week and told his story. Payment on his check was stopped, the con man was arrested, tried, and sentenced to nine months' imprisonment.

2. Demand for payment of a certain fee as a requisite for continued Social Security checks.

Case History: A young man identifying himself as a Social Security "agent" called on a beneficiary in Queens, N. Y. He asked to see her house. He then told her that it looked as if she would not be getting her monthly benefits any more. Pretending sympathy, however, he said, "I'll tell you what I'll do; put $30 in this envelope I'm giving you with this card. Give it to my boss. He'll be here later today." He told her she would get the $30 back in her next check. She put the money in the envelope and was ready to seal it when he said, "Gosh, I forgot, I have to see your gas and light bills too. You get them and I'll lick the envelope for you. I'm in an awful hurry." The widow left the room and returned with the bills a little later. He glanced at them, handed the envelope to her and left. Later the widow thought the envelope was light, she held it up to the window and could see through it and when she opened the envelope she found the card but the money was gone.

3. Invention of a fictitious overpayment.

Case History: Two young men identifying themselves as Social Security agents approached two elderly citizens, aged eighty-six and eighty-four, respectively, and told them there had been an overpayment and the government demanded the excess amount immediately. The eighty-six-year-old beneficiary turned over $750 to the impersonators. The eighty-four-year-old told them he didn't have the $1,628 demanded but that he could have it for them the next day. He then called the Social Security office. The matter was reported to the FBI.

4. A phony survey on how well the current monthly payments meet the beneficiary's needs.

Case History: A well-dressed man called at the home of an aged widow and claimed to be from a Social Security office in Philadelphia. He said he was there to see if her monthly Social Security benefits were large enough to meet her current expenses. He claimed he needed to know what her finances were, and asked to see any valuables, such as jewelry and money that she possessed. After learning where she kept her money, he asked for a drink of water. A few minutes later he hurriedly left, assuring her that her benefit payments would be increased. A short time later, the widow missed $76 she had shown the con man.

There are also the "claims helpers" who assist and otherwise represent elderly people in pursuing their claims for benefits in return for exorbitant or illegal fees.

The following case histories illustrate these frauds.

1. An accountant assisted numerous individuals in establishing entitlement to Social Security benefits by obtaining evidence of earnings, preparing tax returns, etc., for use in connection with their claims. The accountant would give the client the impression that the fee for services was small and the tax high. In this way, the claimant did not know what portion of the total amount was paid for taxes and what portion was the fee for services. Since the man was not an attorney, it was illegal for him to charge a fee in any amount without getting approval.

2. An attorney, acting as a representative for numerous Social Security claimants, accepted money from claimants for his fees—purportedly for the purpose of paying the taxes due. However, he neither filed the tax returns nor paid the taxes.

There are also publications that may deceive or mislead the aged. Because so many people look to Social Security benefits as a major source of income in their old age, there is great public interest in the subject. Many irresponsible publishers offer for sale, at prices ranging from $1.99 to $5, books that cost them about $0.17 a copy to print, but that cannot tell the reader anything basic about the Social Security law that he would not find in the free booklets available at his Social Security office. Some of them do, however, contain advice that, if followed, might result in extensive investigation by the Social Security Administration and thus delay rather than expedite the payment of their Social Security benefits. Following some of the advice contained in these books might place the individual in a worse rather than a better financial position.

Social Security beneficiaries have also complained about persons calling on them who lead them to believe that they, or their firms, are affiliated with the Social Security Administration.

In one instance, a district supervisor for a California insurance company falsely advised an aged social security beneficiary that his company was "backed up" by the Social Security Administration, and if his company could not pay a claim the Social Security Administration would take care of it.

The Social Security Administration uses various informational media to keep its beneficiaries aware of the provisions of the Social Security Act and of their rights and obligations, as well as to caution them of schemes that are designed to defraud them. Pamphlets and check inserts are issued to advise beneficiaries of recently enacted legislation.

If an elderly person has any suspicion of being defrauded, he should get in touch with one of the six-hundred full-time district offices or 4,000 contact stations the Social Security Administration operates throughout the United States.

16   A Potpourri of Con Games:
         How to Spot Them

The Executive Director of the International Association of Police Chiefs, testifying before the Senate Committee on the Aging, stressed that "circumstances" made elderly persons attractive to swindlers.

Among these circumstances are:

(1) Money is the ultimate aim of the con man, and elderly people frequently have lump sums resulting from retirement annuities, lifetime savings, insurance on sales of properties.

(2) Elderly people are frequently unemployed, and with time on their hands they are more accessible to the swindler.

(3) The aged are often lonely and are eager to accept the friendship a seemingly harmless conversation seems to offer.

(4) For some, age has dimmed their perception, making them easy prey for the fast spiel.

(5) Generally, senior citizens tend to be less suspicious and the con man plays on their willingness to help out young people.

All these elements are operative in the myriad of swindles that flow from the con man's fertile mind. Here's how the fleecing is done every day in every part of the United States —and here's how to spot them.

ADVANCE FEE RACKET

According to the U. S. Postal Department, promoters in this area realize millions of dollars each year from businessmen, many of whom are elderly and want to retire.

Method: These racketeers seek their victims by innocent looking circular letters or post cards inquiring, "Is your business for sale?" or "Can you use $1,000 to $5 million?" with advice that, "We may be able to help you." Persons responding are contacted by high-pressure salesmen who, through innuendoes, half truths, and other forms of misrepresentations, lead victims to believe that for the signing of the contract and payment of an advance fee ranging upward from $100, their business could be quickly sold at more than its actual worth.

The contracts are carefully drawn so as to promise only an advertising service. This is fulfilled with glossy, impressive-looking catalogues and similar brochures which are mailed to some legitimate real estate brokers, but which seldom produce actual buyers. There is no written promise to sell the business or refund the money if the company fails. However, the oral sales pitch is full of high-pressure talk designed to lead victims to form such conclusions.

How to Spot: (1) Beware of promises of selling your business at a price you know is far in excess of what it is worth. (2) Give the contract to an attorney before you sign.

VENDING MACHINES, FRANCHISES, AND DISTRIBUTORSHIP

These ugly little schemes are paraded under the heading of "Business Opportunities," "Help Wanted," etc., in daily newspapers and magazines throughout the country, making it appear financial success is certain for an investment upward to $10,000.

Method: Victims are so taken in they often pay part or full payment to these operators without any proof of the company's integrity. Many never receive anything in return. Others, who do, usually find the product is not as represented; locations selected are in out-of-the-way retail establishments; and the exclusive territory and moneymaking opportunities only existed on the glib tongue of the company's salesman or in its advertising literature.

How to Spot: (1) Beware of ads for franchise deals if only a post-office box is given or if the representative who calls has no established office. (2) Check with your lawyer or bank before making any investment.

KNITTING AND SEWING MACHINE RACKETS

Many elderly women with time on their hands, and eager to supplement meager incomes, are easy prey for swindlers.

Method: Victims of this scheme are sought through direct mail and newspaper advertising offering work at home.

Those who respond are called on by high-pressure salesmen who enthuse about the great market demand for home-made garments and tell housewives how easily these garments can be made in their homes. They are assured of earnings up to $25 weekly by selling to outlets furnished by the promoter. To earn this kind of money, one of the firm's machines must be purchased to take advantage of its "buy back" agreement. However, assurances are given that only a few hours' work each day will net an income that can more than cover the cost of the machines.

With the stage set, the housewives sign a conditional sales contract obligating them to pay an exorbitant price for the machine. Usually the promoters buy the garments for a short time, using the early customers as evidence to sell others. Once a particular area becomes saturated, they close up and move on. The housewives find they have a machine of little value and are in hock to a finance company.

Case History: American Knitting Center of West Chicago Inc., defrauded women in the Chicago area of over $400,000 in the sale of imported knitting machines. Many of the 1,200 women swindled were elderly persons who paid up to $550, including finance charges for machines for which the operators paid between $60 and $90.

OTHER WORK-AT-HOME FRAUDS

Many con men do business in nickels and dimes and depend on volume for large profit. Here are three cases (from the files of the U. S. Postal Department), which netted the promoters good profits, and are particularly vicious because they enticed the elderly who could not afford to absorb even small losses.

The L. V. Enterprises at Manchester, N. H., advertised in magazines stating that homeworkers were needed. Those replying were sent a four-page brochure reiterating that workers were needed and that they were "willing to pay for it." When the required $3 was sent in, which was the prime concern of these swindlers, they received an accompanying "Home Instruction Manual" and then learned that it was necessary to own a typewriter and to obtain addresses of new mothers.

Self-Service, Inc. sold catalogues and mailing lists through newspaper ads enticing people to start their own mail-order business—forty-eight victims of this fraud lost $35,000.

Magic Weave, Inc. of Boston advertised in newspapers implying that legitimate jobs were available to women to do hand needlework at home, full or part time. The main objective, however, was to sell cheap kits, worth about $3, for $39.50 and $49.50, after which the victims were on their own and made nothing. It is estimated this work-at-home fraud netted the operators about $100,000.

How to Spot: (1) Beware of companies which use *Help Wanted* columns when there is no offering of employment; (2) beware of the promise of huge profits for part time work, a guaranteed market or a claim that no experience is necessary; (3) beware of testimonials—they are often phonies; (4) beware of promoters who sell kits, instructions or equipment as a prerequisite for the entire operation.

SEX PILLS AND DEVICES

Drugs sold to cure sexual weakness or impotence are a natural for the elderly.

Method: An organization masquerading under a pseudo-scientific name urges readers to submit by mail sums of $10 or $20 for "Stagg Bullets" and "Genuine Passionola," the former for men and the latter for women. The advertisement refers to older men and women who are now able to do what they believed they could not otherwise accomplish because of their advanced years. According to the U. S. Post Office, which succeeded in preventing use of the mails for these products, the words and advertisements for "Stagg" and "Passionola," do not describe the products as blood-builders and tonics but as marvels that can make a man, regardless of age, romantic, young, potent and virile as the gods.

The actual ingredients of "Stagg Bullets" fall into the food-supplement category, containing several of the B vitamins, small amounts of simple carbohydrates, caffein, aspirin, vitamin E and a vitamin C-like product. "Genuine Passionola" contained sugar, juices of pineapple, papaya, peach, apricot, apple, grape, and passion fruit. None of these, it was established, can in any sense overcome the physical or psychic influences which cause lack of sexual vigor or impotency.

Case History: Tigron Distributors, Jersey City, N. J., grossed an estimated $120,000 on claims that its product was a "concrete compound accepted by medical men and scientists: so potent your body will function with the youth energy and sex energy lost in the process of aging." Buyers received only common vitamins.

In addition, the Postal Inspection Service has investigated thousands of mail ads (received primarily by elderly males) for the sale of a variety of drugs which claim to overcome the male partners' inability to develop and maintain more complete and satisfying sexual marital relations. These devices vary in form from so-called splints to large plastic instruments made to simulate the penis to the closest possible detail.

How to Spot: Loss of virility or potency is a medical problem. Perhaps your doctor can help you. See him.

SAVINGS BY MAIL

Elderly persons are often victimized by save-by-mail schemes operated by a number of state-chartered and privately insured savings and loan associations.

Method: These associations advertise nationally, soliciting savings accounts and promising to pay extremely high dividend rates. They also claim that the saving accounts are "insured" by names such as the "Security Financial Insurance Corporation," a name close enough to the federal government's Federal Savings and Loan Insurance Corporation (which assures accounts up to $10,000 each) to lead the unwary into believing that the United States government backs the association.

In effect, there is very little safeguard for funds deposited with these outfits. Large numbers of them have gone bankrupt and their officers indicted on a variety of charges including embezzlement, larceny, and conspiracy to defraud. In most of these instances savers can hope to recover a maximum of 30 per cent of their investments.

The effects of these frauds on the aged were dramatized by some case histories presented to the Senate Subcommittee on Frauds and Misrepresentations Affecting the Elderly by the National Better Business Bureau.

A seventy-year-old Chicagoan had been living on an $85 monthly dividend he had been receiving from a $17,000 savings account with First Capitol Savings and Loan Association. The Association was declared bankrupt and its promoter is now serving time in the penitentiary following his conviction on mail fraud charges.

Another elderly man complained in court that he had accumulated $13,600 in the Mutual Security Savings and Loan Association before it went into receivership. He said he was now a "pauper."

A sixty-six year old woman from New Hampshire said she had more than $22,000 in First Continental Savings and Loan Association which had been placed in receivership.

How to Spot: (1) Beware of schemes that promote savings by mail—especially if your money will be kept in another state or in a foreign country. (2) Beware of the promise of interest rates far above the normal banking or loan association schedules. (3) Beware of offers of expensive free gifts (such as TV sets) as a bonus for starting an account. The account contract usually specifies that you must leave your funds with the association for a year or else the cost of your gift is deducted from your account.

BAIT ADVERTISING

With ads that promise fantastic bargains, fast-moving operators are making fantastic profits. The most prevalent items are automobiles, furs, furniture, home appliances, jewelry, pianos, radio and TV sets, sewing machines, and vacuum cleaners.

Method: A sewing-machine ad offers a "repossessed" brand-new famous-make machine that does everything: fancy stitching, buttonholes, embroidery, darning. A full guarantee is promised and the price is extremely low. It ends with "Call—for our free home demonstration without obligation to buy." When the salesman arrives, he regretfully announces that the machine in the ad has just been sold, but he has with him one every bit as good. He demonstrates and says that his model will cost a mere $2 a week. If the purchaser signs the contract without inquiring how many $2 weeks there will be—or without reading the small print—she will be stuck for $500 for a machine worth less than $100.

How to Spot: (1) Beware of salesmen (in the home or at a store) who try to "switch" you off the original offer made in an ad; (2) demand to know the entire price of the merchandise—not just the weekly or monthly payments; (3) demand that the salesman show you where in the contract the full price is stated.

THE FURNACE SWINDLE

The sales and servicing of home furnaces have long been in the hands of local dealers, the vast majority of whom are reputable businessmen. But for many years, a small minority in this field has fleeced the aged of millions through a vicious selling scheme.

Method: Posing as inspectors or representatives of furnace firms, con men gain entry to the cellar and misrepresent to homeowners that their furnaces are in bad shape; that lethal carbon monoxide gases are escaping; that the furnace is likely to blow up at any minute, or that continued use of the furnace in its present condition will surely result in asphyxiation and death.

As a result, thousands of useful furnaces have been needlessly discarded and replaced at exorbitant prices. For example, the Chicago Better Business Bureau reported the case of a firm that sold the same elderly man two new furnace installations within two years at a total cost of $3,800. The Fort

Wayne Better Business Bureau reported the case of the firm that sold an elderly widow two new furnaces within a three-year period at a cost of $3,847.

How to Spot: (1) Anyone who says he is an official inspector must carry credentials. Ask for these and examine them carefully; (2) if you are told you need a new furnace by one firm, have another dealer examine the furnace—he may have a different opinion.

LUCKY WINNER FRAUDS

A winner can turn into a loser in the twinkling of a con man's eye.

Method: A "nothing to buy" ad offers fabulous prizes to anyone who sends in the coupon. Following the date of the drawing, contestants by the score are informed that they have won a minor prize—perhaps a $100 coupon toward the purchase of a color TV set. When the lucky winner comes to the shop, he is given the TV along with a "warranty" contract to sign. The contract sets the price of the TV—minus the $100 coupon—at $800, or double its competitive cost.

How to Spot: (1) If a company says its coupon is "good now or never" there's a good chance the firm can't afford investigation; (2) beware of "prizes" good only in conjunction with the spending of additional money; (3) don't sign any contract or warranty without taking it home to read it carefully and out of earshot of the salesman.

HEARSE CHASERS

Many schemes and "promotions" are designed to prey on the recently bereaved, which frequently includes the elderly. "Hearse Chasers" victimize survivors by collecting for merchandise which is falsely represented as having been ordered by the deceased. Some render bills when nothing is owed. Some claim part payment has been made by the deceased and demand the alleged balance. Other promoters make a living by mailing unordered merchandise such as religious items and plastic-sealed copies of death notices. Another favorite is an offer to include the deceased in a biographical book. Acceptance leads to the discovery that survivors have contracted to pay high prices for engravings, reprints, and other extras.

How to Spot: (1) Demand to see the signature on any supposed order for merchandise; (2) keep in mind that in a state of grief you may consent to arrangements you might regret at a later date.

DANCE STUDIOS

There are many examples of how old folks are high-pressured and sweet-talked into paying large sums of money to a handful of dance studio operators for lessons which they might or might not live to enjoy. In the main, the slick promoter plays on the desire of elderly widows and spinsters for flattering attention and the emotional satisfaction this brings to an otherwise lonely existence.

Method: Swindling in this area is made possible through the device of the "lifetime" memberships, whereby a studio contracts to provide several thousand hours of instruction to an elderly person on a paid-in-advance basis. Victims have reported to the Better Business Bureaus that they have been bilked out of their life's savings for "lifetime" membership and multiple "lifetime" memberships. Here are some typical cases.

A dance studio signed a sixty-nine year old widow to eight

"lifetime" memberships, entitling her to 3,100 hours of instruction at a cost of $34,913.

A seventy-one-year-old woman mortgaged her home to make the final payment to a dance studio on several "lifetime" memberships totaling $32,600. She bought one of the memberships while in the hospital with a knee injury which made it doubtful she would ever walk again, let alone dance.

A seventy-four-year-old widow brought suit against a dance studio to recover $25,000 she paid for 2,480 hours of dance instruction. She was promised attractive male dancing partners and was assured that the lessons would make her a gifted dancer so that she could perform on television.

In a period of five months, one dance studio sold a woman three "life" memberships at $6,800 each, totaling $20,640. The third and last one was to perpetuate the memory of her late husband by giving free dance lessons to deserving persons.

A seventy-nine-year-old woman paid $11,800—half of her total savings—for lifetime lessons. When a grand jury heard her tale of woe, a grand larceny indictment was returned.

How to Spot: Never sign a contract with a dance studio without taking it home and reading it carefully—or, preferably, showing it to a lawyer. If the contract is a swindle, the studio won't let you remove it from the premises, so a request is all that is needed.

LONELY HEARTS CLUBS

Most of these clubs offer personal introductions to members of the opposite sex in the same age bracket. They do not deliver, and charge anywhere from $50 to $200.

Method: Pocketing the initial fee is usually all these operators are after. If the subscriber calls to investigate, he is told to exercise patience while the vast staff of the club sorts out the "right" person for a match.

There are also correspondence clubs which take initial deposits and sometimes go much further.

Method: An elderly gentleman receives delightful letters from a widow across the country found for him by the correspondence club. After a few months of writing, the widow declares her intention to visit the gentleman. However, in transit, she falls seriously ill and cables him for a bundle of money—just until she can get to her own bank and make a withdrawal. The money is wired and that is the last that is heard of the not-so-sick widow.

How to Spot: In general, such operations should be avoided. There are adequate special centers and facilities for older people to get acquainted. A few inquiries about these could save a lot of money.

PHONY INVESTIGATORS

There are all sorts of swindlers whose gimmick is to scare older people into handing out money by telling them they've underpaid Maintenance Tax or Medicare and demanding immediate payment. Other investigators pose as bank examiners, FBI agents, or whatever official capacity will do the job.

Method: The method is as varied as the disguises, but essentially it involves getting the money under a false pretext and even leaving a phony receipt.

How to Spot: If approached in person or by telephone by anyone who claims to be an official representative of a government body or local institution, ask for credentials or say you will phone him back. Then check him out with the local FBI office or your local police.

SPECIAL PRICE OFFERS

These deals usually involve use of a "new" product on a house at a reduced price in exchange for allowing the contractor to use the home as a display model for his product.

Method: A home owner is given aluminum siding at a special price in exchange for permission to display. However, the small print in the contract also gives the promoter a mortgage or deed of trust to the home. Thus, he can sell the house if payments for the siding jobs are not made. The amount is usually exorbitant—many times in excess of $5,000.

How to Spot: (1) Get the address of the contractor's company and phone to see if he's authorized to make such an offer; (2) make sure that any guarantees that are given orally are also in print; (3) read the contract carefully and make sure you get a complete and legible carbon copy signed by the salesman; (4) most of the legitimate businesses do not send their salesmen out to ring doorbells. It would be best not to do business with any of these.

GYPSY SWINDLERS

Many door-to-door confidence men exploit the elderly to the tune of millions annually through a variety of schemes. Here are some favorite schemes culled from the files of Better Business Bureaus throughout the country.

In Texas, three swindlers filched almost $4,000 from an eighty-nine-year-old woman over a period of a few months. Con man "A" called, posing as a city inspector, and told her that her storm sewers needed cleaning to pass city inspection. He worked two hours and charged her $1,050. Four days later con man "B" called and claimed to be a roofing inspector. He insisted that the roof needed painting and repair. He and an assistant did the job in less than one day and charged $1,685. About two months later, the third swindler called, posing as a city wire inspector. He said the wiring in the attic needed repair. He got the job, performed it in twenty minutes and charged $1,250.

In Missouri, a retired physician in his eighties gave a representative of an alleged termite-control firm $1,790 for treating his home after being shown a piece of termite-eaten wood supposedly removed from his basement. Subsequent investigation failed to establish that there was any termite activity in the home.

An eighty-one-year-old widow was solicited by an alleged tree surgeon to work on her elm trees. He charged her $1,854. Several experts stated the work done was either unnecessary or detrimental to the trees.

A fifty-eight-year-old widow in South Carolina, whose only income is her monthly Social Security check, was high-pressured into signing a contract for aluminum siding at a cost of $70 per month for eighty-four months for a total of $5,880. A local contractor said the job could be done for $660.

In Idaho, a slick "health insurance" agent grabbed $100 to $200 for health and accident coverage. The buyers never received any policy. Later an accomplice would call, say he was investigating the salesman, and request their receipts—leaving them with no proof of money paid.

A seventy-one-year-old woman in Paterson, New Jersey, was told by a man claiming to be a public service employee that there had been a break in the main gas line and he wanted to check the pipes in her basement. After doing so, he called the woman to the basement and demonstrated by lighting matches that gas was leaking around the meter. He explained that the pipes were burned out and needed repair, the cost of which would be a nice, even $1,000. The woman went to her bank and withrew ten $100 bills and gave them to the swindler. He promised to return in the afternoon to do the job, but never showed up. A subsequent check established that he had tampered with the meter so as to make it leak.

"SOMETHING FOR NOTHING"

There are many "something for nothing" gimmicks. For example, the man with a bolt of cloth may say he is a British sailor "just off the boat," implying that he by-passed customs with his fine import; a man offering furs poses as a Canadian fur trapper who has eluded the Border Patrol; a man offers to oil the shingles on the roof for a special low price because he "just happens to be in the neighborhood and has just enough material for one more job"; a girl offering lace says it was made in Scotland by her dear old grandmother but must be sacrificed at a great loss to help pay for the old lady's hospitalization, etc. etc.

With their thick brogues and highly developed artistry these con artists and their fellow swindlers have palmed off a wide variety of sleazy products and services at prices far in excess of their market value.

17 | Stopping the Swindler: Young Plus Old

As we have seen, the nineteen million people in our nation aged sixty-five and over are prime targets for an infinite variety of confidence men. Their aches and pains, their need for extra income, their hope for a retirement home in the sun, and their loneliness which quickly reacts to attention offered by sympathetic salesmen, make them easy pickings for the unscrupulous.

It is a terribly unequal battle. A lonely, uninformed target against a well-organized, glib and experienced team of swindlers.

The Federal Trade Commission—with almost six decades of halting unfair business competition—has become truly expert in how law violators operate. Here's how it suggests the young can help the old, how children can help their parents and grandparents protect themselves from being victimized.

The initial step is to sit down with the senior citizen to evaluate the bland assurances and promises offered. Not being subject to the same degree of temptation for the product being offered and not being the direct target of the salesman's charm (whether it be his words and manner, or the language of a tricky advertisement), sons, daughters, and younger friends can offer valuable assistance in determining whether the goods or services are worth the money. If the sellers can pool their talents, so can you. Your combined investigation, judgment and experience might well prevent the loss of precious savings by those whose age denies them opportunity to replace it. Indeed, sons and daughters might be confronted with making up the loss.

The monetary toll is not the only one. The disreputable tout spurious substitutes for proper medical treatment, steal time and effort on phony income-producing schemes, and reward hope for a happier existence during the sunset years with disillusionment and bitterness, if not tragedy.

The reputable business community also suffers. Offering needed services and products and genuine opportunities—all at fair prices—it is unjust that their efforts and their advertising be ignored or devalued simply because a small minority of overly eager sellers would destroy confidence in any kind of claim.

Younger people should seek and maintain the confidence of aging parents and older friends as to what their needs and desires are. If the relationship can be built up to the point where they will confide any plan to invest their savings to better their situation, the plan can at least be studied and assessed more thoroughly. Law violators will have lost immediately their biggest advantage, namely, to deal with isolated individuals and to play on their hopes and fears.

It is one thing for them to get a trusting signature on a contract when the signer makes his or her decision without first confiding in children or trusted friends; it is quite another matter if the older person first invites others to make a check on the proposition. The latter situation is exactly what the suave and kindly seeming salesman and his boss do *NOT* want. They will argue that opportunity cannot wait, that the sands of time are running out, that their offer is a limited one, and that countless other "mature investors" are lolling in comfort and gratitude for having made a similar investment.

What are the false or misleading claims devised especially to appeal to the elderly? The FTC has found that the following are time-tested favorites (although experience has shown that new ones are born as fast as opportunity offers.) Here are the principal ones to keep an eye on in the interest of those you need and who need you:

THE HEALTH CLAIMS

Sons and daughters and friends of elderly people can join forces with them in stiffening their defenses against medical quackery, whether it be "cures" for arthritis and cancer (which they may actually have or only fear they have), or high-speed mail-order "bargain" cures for other diseases, including those of the eyes and ears, that require proper diagnosis and treatment.

Step 1 is to invite and to listen attentively to a description that the elderly person can give of his ailment. Because most people of any age are all too eager to discuss their pains, the temptation exists to let their complaints go in one ear and out the other. Such indifference invites the sufferer to seek his own solution, which is exactly what the illegal few count on.

Step 2 is to urge that diagnosis of any persistent ailment be made by competent medical authority, rather than an acquaintance "who had exactly the same trouble," or the sweeping assurances of many an advertisement.

Step 3 is to persist in Step 2. Sound advice, given but once, can too easily be ignored.

THE EXTRA-INCOME CLAIMS

Knowing that many elderly people are hard-pressed to stretch their retirement income to cover even the barest necessities, the fast-buck operators are all too ready to sell, at a cruel price, false hope for extra income.

In its investigation and prosecution of scores of cases, the FTC has discovered a pattern to these deceptive offers. The initial approach to the victim is by an advertisement promising excellent, even spectacular, profits for easy spare time work. Frequently the ad appears in "Help Wanted" columns of a newspaper. But invariably there is a small requirement before the victim can commence collecting the exciting reward for his part-time labors. This is that he makes a substantial investment in the enterprise. Usually it is described as an investment in inventory or in a vending machine.

Here are typical ads the FTC has ordered stopped:

"YOUR NET PROFITS approximately 100%,
and on some of our machines the net profit may
be 200 to 300%!"

"The Safest, Surest Business on Earth."
"No RISK of losing your investment."
"$400 to $500 MONTHLY POSSIBLE...applicant
must have car, references and $600 to $1,200
working capital which is secured by inventory...
Work only 8 to 10 hours a week!"
"Your $800 to $1,500 investment GUARANTEED
TO produce $200 to $250 a month!"

How can you detect which are the spurious offers for extra income?

In the first place, you must shut your own eyes and ears to the golden promises and force yourself to do a little cold-blooded investigating. If the "opportunity" involves selling a product, you would do well to make a market test of your own—contact the people you think might be interested in buying such a product and find out what they have to say. It would also be worth your while to ask the owners of competing products and discover what kind of competition would confront you. In the case of vending machines, you might well ask the operators of popular restaurants and stores in your neighborhood how eager they would be to have an elderly person place a vending machine in their establishment and be responsible for servicing it. And as a double check on your own market testing, you would do well to talk the proposition over with your banker or a representative of the Better Business Bureau, and, if neither is available, ask the opinions of the men and women in your community whose business judgment you most respect on what they think of the idea.

Armed with the answers you most likely will get, you

can argue persuasively for a safer use of the precious savings of our senior citizens.

LANDS IN THE SUN

Having escaped from the treadmill of earning a living, many a retired man and his wife also would like to escape winter and join others of about the same age and inclinations in the playlands of our nation. The reputable majority of the real estate industry is able to accommodate their desires. But when enough of our citizens are beset by such heady aspirations and have the money to make their dreams come true, a few sellers, more careless with the truth, are ready to accommodate them.

In advising the elderly person whose appetite for a retirement home has been whetted by the advertising of a mail-order land developer, you would do well to consult first with a lawyer or someone else who is well versed in real estate and then get the answers to these questions at the very least:

(1) Does the state in which the land is located have a law requiring full disclosure of pertinent facts concerning land developments? If so, an effort should be made to inspect a copy of the real estate developer's report to that state's real estate commission. It may not be as easy reading as the sales brochure, but it contains vital information. Fewer than half the states have such a law. However, such retirement favorites as California, Arizona, New Mexico and Hawaii, do.

(2) Does the salesman have any actual photographs of the land to contrast with the artists' conceptions of what the property *might* someday resemble?

(3) How far distant is the land illustrated in the literature from that which is being offered?

(4) Who drew the map of the real estate development?

Is it, too, an artist's conception? Or does it make the property offered for sale appear to be more accessible and closer to vital services and conveniences than is the fact?

(5) Are distances described as "minutes away" or in miles over travelable roads?

(6) Has the literature disclosed anything about such subjects as flash floods, windstorms, sandstorms, temperature extremes, altitude, or water depth?

(7) Does the contract contain a nonacceleration clause which prevents taking of title and deed before it suits the developer's convenience or his ability to release his mortgage or get subdivision approval?

(8) Has the senior citizen been given information on exactly what improvements will be installed—and when? And is the information in the contract?

(9) If there is a money-refund assurance given, is it necessary to travel all the way to the property to get it?

(10) If the seller guarantees that you can transfer your payments to buy a different lot (for example, to get closer to a glimpse of mankind or to vital services), how much more is the preferred location going to cost?

(11) Have you and your senior citizen really read the purchase contract—not just the bold type that the seller would like to have you read, but the fine print containing information presented in the dullest possible way? Hopeful eyes have the capacity to see only what they are encouraged to see.

Finally, if your investigation convinces you that scurrilous salesmanship is being used to sell retirement property, you would do well to pass on what information you have gained to the Better Business Bureau, to the real estate commission of the state involved, to the U. S. Post Office Department, to the Securities and Exchange Commission, or to the Federal Trade Commission. By this you can make a real contribution to the protection of others, both young and old.

MAIL-ORDER HEALTH INSURANCE

It would be hard to find any field in which your teamwork with elderly people would be more beneficial than in the cautious purchase of mail-order health insurance. Most of this is legitimate, and it provides a most welcome safeguard for those purchasing it.

It also provides a made-to-order situation for the illegal fringe operators who would come to the "rescue" with mail order insurance at "low cost, no exam, comprehensive hospital and medical coverage, no ifs, ands, or buts, no limitations . . . all for pennies a day!"

Fortunately, the gyp outfits are very much in the minority, but theirs are the claims and omissions that dangle the brightest promises to the elderly, even to the extent of persuading some of them to take the tragic step of abandoning higher cost, but certainly higher benefit protection. Too late do they discover that the protection they think they have bought exists only in their minds and not in the fine print of the misrepresented policies.

Here is a sampling from the bag of tricks, things for which you and your elderly parents and friends should be on the lookout:

The health-insurance advertising might fail to disclose exceptions, reductions, or limitations of the policy. It also might conveniently fail to mention that there is a waiting or probationary period before health benefits become payable.

Or that they are payable only when certain conditions occur and what these conditions are.

The ads might fail also to mention what effect pre-existing conditions of health may have on the insurance coverage, or that the policy applies only to a certain age group.

You would do well, too, to explore whether the advertising has failed to disclose all the terms affecting renewability, cancelability, or termination of the policy. And do the ad's golden promises refer to the benefits of one policy or more than one?

The cautious buyer also would want to double check to learn if the mail order advertising squares with the facts as to whether the health of the insured is not a factor in determining if he can be insured or what benefits would be paid. The same holds for claims that no medical examination is required; or, if none is required, what limitations are put on the policy's protection?

A go-slow warning shows up when you encounter a sales pitch that employs such words as "up to" and "as high as" in describing how much money will be paid in dollars. Such amounts might be very much the exception and paid only for the treatment of rare diseases.

In short, you would do well to advise the senior citizen to hold off buying mail-order insurance until he knows exactly what he's going to get for his money.

Granted that an insurance policy is hard reading (and requires better eyesight than bold-type advertising), your careful reading of it could provide a great service to the senior citizen you want to help. And if you would like a synopsis of its possible pitfalls by a trained eye, the chances are better

than even that any reputable insurance agent would be glad
to accommodate you.

<h2 style="text-align:center">MISCELLANEOUS DANGERS</h2>

Although the foregoing types of deception are of particular
concern to the elderly, this does not mean our senior citizens are
not victimized by other schemes whose targets include the
young as well as the old.

Vanity publishers also exact a toll from both young and
old, with the latter being given special attention. Often senior
citizens have long been nursing a desire to write a book as
soon as they achieve the leisure to do so, or, as frequently
happens, a widow is anxious that the world recognize by
means of a book the stature and wisdom of her departed
husband. These understandable desires will be accommodated
by the so-called "vanity press" for a price.

There is, of course, nothing wrong with subsidized book
publishing. Many a book whose subject material is of limited
interest could not otherwise be published. Where the chicanery
creeps in is when the publisher understates the true nature
of his business. Instead of revealing that the expense of publishing the book (plus a profit to the publisher) will be paid
entirely by the person wanting to get it published, the impression is created that the book's merits are such that it could
make money, even become a best-seller. There have been
instances where publishers have concocted the most flattering
readers' reports on hopeless to mediocre manuscripts solely
to entice the would-be writer (or his widow) to invest in
the book's publication.

Admittedly, it is difficult for you who are consulting with
your elderly father, mother, or friend, to say that the book
they want published does not have the sales possibilities the

vanity publisher implies it does. However, you can try. And one way to do this is to urge that the manuscript be submitted to any number of reputable publishers in the certain knowledge they will reject it if it has no merit.

There is also deception in the advertising of some correspondence schools. While the vast majority give students their money's worth in education and training, there are always a few concerned primarily with collecting fees for their study "courses" with little or no regard for whether the student is even qualified to commence the course, much less learn anything from it. Their advertising, however, skips over any requirements a prospective student should have and concentrates instead on the high salaried jobs graduates might expect.

To the elderly these flamboyant claims offer hope of augmenting their income. For example, the FTC has brought action to halt advertising that a mail order course of instruction would qualify a graduate (regardless of her age) to become a hospital nurse, when in fact no hospital would accept such credentials.

It would require from you only a minimum of investigation to get a useful opinion from a school authority or a person engaged in the profession concerned on whether the senior citizen by completing such a course of study might indeed be able to find employment in that field. It behooves you to do this, for the phony correspondence course is one of the cruelest of all deceptions; it robs the victim not only of money but of time and hope.

These are the principal areas of deception which might trap the elderly. There are others too, and still others yet to be conceived. Some are obviously dangerous, and to a cautious person they are palpably phony, but their advertising is not addressed to the skeptical but to the fears and hopes of the credulous and the desperate.

Where deception has snared a victim, it is usually too late or too costly to get a refund of the money invested, if indeed it is possible to find the perpetrator of the trick. Many of them are aware that their operations can ill afford a fixed address where suit could be brought against them. In other cases, their defense can be based successfully on the fine print of a contract that their victims failed to read. And the best that such organizations as the Better Business Bureau can do is to identify the illegal scheme and those who engage in it. City and state authorities can levy fines and imprison if their ordinances and laws empower them to do so. The Federal government can also bring stern measures to bear, although the Federal Trade Commission has authority only to issue orders to cease and desist from the illegality. Only if its orders are violated can it seek fines of up to $5,000 for each violation.

To punish the law violators is small compensation to the elderly man or woman who has been victimized. Far better that the senior citizen avoid the pitfall in the first place.

Here is where the sons, and daughters and friends can be of greatest help. By teaming up with those you love, by inviting their confidence in your judgment before instead of after they invest their time and money, by doing the investigating they may not be able to do, and by quieting as often as necessary the siren song of temptation, you can save them money and heartache.

You can become the team the con men can't beat.

18 | Educating the Elderly Consumer: The Government's Role

Recent federal actions on behalf of elderly consumers has put heavy emphasis on educational programs and other actions that will help states to do the same. The latest report by the Special Senate Committee on Aging provides a roundup of these efforts.

William Bechill, Commissioner of the Administration on the Aging, reported to the Senate Committee on Aging that the AOA is supporting pilot demonstrations in ten areas of great concern to older Americans: (1) sound nutrition, (2) economy food purchasing, (3) the careful purchase of credit, (4) avoidance of quackery, (5) avoidance of fraudulent products and practices, (6) safe and effective use of drugs, (7) accident prevention, (8) management of retirement income, (9) Medicare and supplementary health insurance plans, and (10) care of clothing and household equipment.

He also said that approximately sixty projects approved for funding had elements of consumer protection. A later report from AOA noted that a majority of senior activity centers funded under Title III of the Older Americans Act have an element of education in their services.

One noteworthy example of direct help to consumers was provided by a program supported by the New York State Office for the Aging under the Older Americans Act. A full-time consumer specialist is now at work in a center serving a large number of elderly in a Manhattan public housing project. In testimony before the Subcommittee on Health of the Elderly, the director gave many examples of difficulties caused by misunderstanding of Medicare, Medicaid and Social Security. The director also gave his account of the project status:

> The program has (1) demonstrated a need for adequate food programs, (2) cooperated in a Medicaid alert, (3) developed a drug plan, (4) attempted to involve older people in social action, (5) initiated an information program with welfare, (6) held a citywide conference on consumer problems of older people, and (7) begun testing various educational techniques. Our next year will be focused on social action and the development of a family security program.

Another approach to consumer education of the elderly

was provided during September and October of 1967 by *Project Money-Wise Senior,* which was conducted in Boston, Massachusetts by the Bureau of Federal Credit Unions under the sponsorship of the Massachusetts Commission on Aging and the Consumers Council of the Bay State. An AOA report on the project makes these observations:

> "The agenda of the four-week consumer program included an overview of the effects of poverty on the elderly, marketing and shopping weaknesses of the older poor, recognition of fraudulent practices, financial counseling and budgeting, use of credit, and discussions of available public services."
>
> The executive secretary of the Massachusetts Commission on Aging, John T. Sweeney, stated: "It is our opinion that *Project Money-Wise Senior* is one of the most important and worthwhile projects that the Massachusetts Commission on Aging has ever been involved in. Without exception, every single participant derived great benefit from this program and they have returned to their community groups, not only better informed for themselves, but in a position to assist others in making sure that senior citizens get the most products and services for their meager incomes. I believe that it would be of inestimable value to the senior citizens of this country and their communities if this project was conducted in every State in the Union.
>
> "The commission plans to follow-up on *Project Money-Wise Senior* by placing the older participants in Title III projects, senior citizens' organizations, and consumer groups in their comumunities."

Working in consultation with the AOA, the Food and Drug

Administration is conducting widespread conferences on "The Older Citizen in Today's Market Place." The purpose of those conferences as expressed in *FDA Papers* is "to penetrate the world of our elderly citizens and bring to their doorsteps awareness of the new medicine, the new foods, and the new hazards of the marketplace."

State agencies on aging are working with the FDA and, in some cases, acting on their own to hold conferences on such issues as quackery and buying practices.

Seven federal agencies are cooperating in an intensive study intended to explore types of consumer response to claims made for worthless or questionable health products. The survey was first recommended in a report by a unit of the Senate Committee on Aging and is now nearing the end of its first phase. It is anticipated that the study will be completed during the coming year.

FTC Chairman Paul Rand Dixon reported that the Commission is intensifying its efforts on all consumer complaints related to health products. While recognizing that primary responsibility in this area rests with the FDA, he said he "is not at all unmindful that the Commission also bears a direct and substantial responsibility in this respect." In 1967, the FTC and FDA worked to explore and develop coordinated programs for maximum effectiveness of each agency.

Some reasons for the FTC concern in this area were expressed in an excerpt from a Commission cease-and-desist order submitted by Mr. Dixon:

"The need for protection of the public becomes particularly acute where misrepresentations are made with respect to health claims and the efficacy of drugs since the appeal of such representations falls most poignantly on those persons who are in distress, frequently the aged and the infirm.

"Moreover, today, with Medicare a reality, many people may be consulting doctors for the first time in their lives. They will be learning that aches and pains and discomforts of all kinds may be symptoms of diseases which they had never heard of before or never before associated with their own distress.

"Consequently, advertised claims of drug efficacy will have increasing relevance to this segment of our population and will offer hope of relief to millions in our population who may have previously ignored such advertising not realizing their possible application to their own conditions."

An entirely new field of study was suggested during hearings before the Senate Committee on Aging by Mrs. Geneva Mathiasen, Executive Director of the National Council on the Aging:

"... Our society is not sufficiently aware of the older group as consumers and the amount of money they spend in the aggregate.

"There is little doubt that older people are adversely affected by the current preoccupation of producers and purveyors of consumers goods with the 'Pepsi generation' in spite of the fact that there are nearly two million more people in the United States today who are sixty and over than there are teen-agers. In the aggregate,... people over sixty-five... spend between $35 and $40 billion. While many individuals are poor, a few are very rich, and a good number are well to do. Their incomes are increasing. It is estimated that in ten years this will be a $55 billion market. At present, it is not being exploited either by the producers or by the sellers of goods.

"The National Council on the Aging, concerned with the overall well-being of older people, believes that their needs will be met in part by health and welfare services, but also by the production and marketing of consumer goods suited to their special requirements and readily available."

Mrs. Esther Peterson, then Special Assistant to the President on Consumer Affairs, made a similar point:

"Much marketing effort today is directed at developing special products for that segment of our population that is young. This is entirely proper. But I think that industry would do well to examine... what products merit special design for the elderly."

Congressional authority to influence product design and development is limited, as it should be. But the Senate Committee on Aging feels it can perform a function by encouraging public discussion of this matter and by suggesting certain actions by federal agencies that may have possible effects for the elderly consumer of all income groups and for manufacturers and providers of services and housing. Arguments for such action were well expressed by Mrs. Mathiasen:

"For many years, NCOA has directed attention to a number of areas where the inventiveness which characterizes modern industrial design and engineering might be utilized to help create a living environment conducive to the well-being of individuals as they grow older, to help them retain independence and perform their daily tasks with less effort, and to enjoy with greater zest their leisure time. Whether a dress has a zipper up the back or up the front may make the difference between a woman's being able to dress herself or not. The simple act of rising from a a chair, or getting in and out of a taxicab, can add or subtract years to a man's apparent age, depending on how the chair or taxicab is designed."

A case can also be made for the fact that better design—particularly in public buildings and transportation facilities—helps all people, including those who may have a disability of some kind. Alan R. Logan, chairman of the Governor's Committee on Employment of the Handicapped in Florida, discussed that point:

"All elderly are in some degree physically limited. But all physically limited people are not elderly. The public is all of the people and all things "public" should be truly that."

Among other suggestions presented to the Senate Committee on Aging were:

Design of clothing: Mrs. Dorothy Behrens, designer-director of vocational guidance and rehabilitation services in Cleveland, said that a study of clothing available for elderly women in that area yielded only "poorly designed, uninteresting clothing in monotonous patterns and unsuitable colors in limited sizes for older women—as younger women's measurements were used as a standard for patterns."

Over the years, the Department of Agriculture, through its home economics studies, has interested itself in this special problem. In 1939-40, the USDA made a nationwide study of body measurements for women in the eighteen, nineteen, and twenty-year-old brackets, with modest additional samples in middle-aged groups.

In the late 1950's, the USDA undertook a study of clothing for handicapped women. Special apparel were designed for the handicapped and exhibits of these specially designed clothes were made available for inspection by interested consumer groups and manufacturers. This body of knowledge was not, however, put to use by the clothing industry. Mrs. Behrens' Cleveland agency did adopt these designs, operating in part with public funds.

Recently, the Department of Agriculture entered into a three-year contract with Boston University for a study of the body measurements of women in the seventy to seventy-nine-age bracket. This study will be completed in June 1970.

The USDA also provides clothing design assistance through the auspices of its Extension Service, through instruction and the distribution of design materials.

The Senate Committee on Aging feels that this area of clothing design is one that requires attention if the consumer needs of the elderly are to be met. It has recommended that the Administration on Aging take on the task of bringing together sufficient consumer statistics so that manufacturers of clothing could be encouraged to produce such items of wearing apparel in the retail clothing market.

Living arrangements: Many older Americans move from houses they have owned most of their adult lives into smaller apartments. Often, major adjustments must be made. An experimental apartment—outfitted by the American Association of Retired Persons in consultation with national trade associations and Mrs. Peterson—demonstrated that even crowded quarters can be furnished at modest cost.

Testimony before the Senate Committee on Aging by Mr. Edward H. Noakes, a member of an American Institute of Architects study group, raised some fundamental questions about the planning of apartments:

> "With a little thought, apartments generally could be planned with kitchens whose counters, sinks, ovens, and storage could all be adjusted up or down with the use of a screwdriver, their bathrooms could have walls designed to take one or any combination of grab-bars. Such apartments would be a godsend to people who want to live independently but can't find the environment."

Haley Sofge, director of the Miami Housing Authority, told of practical lessons he learned in day-to-day experience:

> "...there is much still to be learned in the design of apartments suitable to the needs of the elderly. All federal programs concerned with elderly housing are still subject to evaluation as to the design and use of materials, in particular in the kitchen and the bath. For instance, in dealing with the elderly person who needs a refrigerator we actually found that he needed a larger refrigerator due to the fact that he was limited in his ability to shop. The elderly wait for a welfare check and they do not make too many trips to the store. When they do, they bring home a large amount of groceries at one time. It may be possible to develop a special top burner and oven for the elderly, with built-in safety features, and the volume of elderly housing may warrant such a study by industry. In fact,

industry has a role here and possibly we should interest industry in special design studies of elderly needs in terms of furniture, bath and kitchen equipment—and I am not speaking of an institutional design but one that would assist the elderly."

Clearly, there is more room for experimentation and discussion about the design of apartments and fixtures used in federally assisted housing accommodations for the elderly.

Furniture design also received the Committee's attention. Dr. Michale M. Dasco, director of Goldwater Hospital Service in New York City, who has conducted studies on furniture design and its relation to physical well-being of the elderly stressed that health scientists and furniture manufacturers should engage in extensive consultation:

"It has been repeatedly pointed out that with advancing years skill, strength, and sensory functional capacity are diminished, even in the absence of any identifiable disease. The combination of these factors create a situation which presents a considerable safety hazard. Therefore, in addition to practicality and esthetic appearance the furniture designer must constantly bear in mind the importance of safety provisions. These safety measures will have to be considered not only in the design and construction of furniture but also in the materials used. In considering the need for designing a new type of furniture for elderly people I do not believe there is any question about the need for intimate cooperation between the furniture designer, manufacturer, and those who are by the very nature of their profession acquainted with the physical and emotional demands of the elderly person. It must be recognized that in addition to the architect, the furniture designer is in the best position to alter the elderly person's physical environment to suit his comfort and functional needs. The need for cooperation is so obvious that one often wonders why it has not been recognized before. It is hoped that a promising cooperation between health scientists and furniture designers will develop in the future, resulting in additional constructive steps to make the elderly person's life safer and more comfortable."

Architectural barriers: A term used to describe any design deficiency that reduces accessibility to a building or any other public facility, such as a subway or a pedestrian walkway over a road. Mr. Noakes, who is chairman of an AIA project to eliminate such barriers, told the Senators that more careful planning is required in our public buildings so that they can accommodate the nonaverage man—in this case, the handicapped or elderly person.

"It may not be the height of folly to continue to build and construct for the average man, but it is certainly out of step with modern social, medical, political science to ignore the needs and aspirations of the millions who are temporarily or permanently incapable of adapting to average design conditions, to say nothing about the added burden on the public treasury."

"There are also legal and moral overtones when taxpayers are excluded, by design, from the enjoyment of a publicly financed venture such as the rapid rail system now being designed for Washington, D. C."

19 | The Year Two Thousand:
Twenty-Eight Million Senior Citizens

Population projections about future generations of older Americans tell only part of the story of vast social and economic change that can be expected within the next three decades, as more Americans reach retirement age than ever before, and as those Americans live additional years in retirement.

To explore the ramifications of such growth, the Senate Committee on Aging called "a convocation of experts" in December 1967. Two major conclusions emerged from these deliberations:

1. Tomorrow's population of older Americans will be far different in needs and expectations from today's.

2. To prepare for great changes ahead, authoritative and comprehensive projections of future requirements should be made in such areas as retirement income, housing and other shelter needs including nursing homes and alternatives, health facilities and care, and new kinds of social services.

Asked by the Committee to make some observations about the changing composition and outlook of the elderly population during the next few decades, Prof. Robert Morris, of Brandeis University, gave this foretaste of what the year 2000 may bring:

"Reliable prediction about the next 35 years is quite impossible because too little is known about the conditions which will shape the future. However, if present trends continue at a relatively even pace, and barring major catastrophes, the following guesses are not wholly unreasonable.

"1. The U. S. population will be approximately 310 million of whom 30 million will be over the age of 65. Approximately two-thirds of this total, or 20 million persons, will be over the age of 75. It is this latter group, over 75, which consumes health, hospital, and nursing services most heavily; the group in which older persons are least able to care for themselves.

"2. At least 16 million of all persons over 65 will be single persons, having never married, or the widowed or divorced. Three million will lack extensive family ties and the deep and intensive family relationships upon which we are accustomed to rely in periods of illness or disability. (Over 10 per cent will be divorced or never married.)

"3. The average life expectancy for adults who reach age 65 will not be much higher than it is today.... Women who are longer lived can expect to live at least to 80 as an average.

"4. The ratio of surviving males to females is expected to drop much further, from 76.9 in 1965 to 73 in the year 2000. More than ever the problems of age will be dominated by the special needs of aged women.

"5. Our technical achievements in the production of goods may reduce the average age for retirement to 60 years. There are already some hundreds of thousands of persons who retire from their major careers before the age of 60. This once happened because of illness, now it is due to the generosity of industrial retirement plans for executive personnel and national generosity for members of the Armed Forces and... civil servants.

"6. A combination of the last two estimates means that, for the average American, between 15-20 years of human life—and more likely 20 than 15 years—one fourth of man's time on earth—becomes "free time" detached from goods-producing labor. Twenty years of time, for the average human being, who must decide what he shall do with his life, rather than having a brief span at the end of a working career to ask 'what *have* I done with my life?'

"7. The price level will be 50 per cent higher than it is today, given a non-inflationary cycle and the recent rate of 'creeping inflation....' Individuals who accumulate their economic reserve through insurance and social security during the next 30 years, at current price levels, will be faced with a substantial gap between income and prices by the year 2000.

"8. The rapid tempo of social and economic and technological change in America will probably continue and even increase. This will isolate the aged more than ever. The American population will be more mobile than ever before. It will be necessary for most adults to consider one or more changes in jobs and careers throughout their adult lives. Families will move more frequently than they do today.

Even now, on the average, 20 per cent of the urban population changes housing each year, but only half as many persons over 65 move. Constant family moving at this rate leaves the aged behind. It becomes more and more difficult for neighborhoods and families to maintain and sustain the social and physical well-being of older persons who live more and more among strangers.

"9. The average aged in 30 years will be much more like the average middle-aged or youthful adult today. Most will have had a high school education and almost half will have had some college education. They will be native born, reared in a growing, mobile and expectant society and will have many advanced skills. This contrasts with the present aged, who, as a group are weighted by immigrant origin, have a grade school education or less, who were reared in a slower and more frugal world, and who are less skilled.

"The golden age center of today will hardly satisfy the college educated oldster of the year 2000. Neither will present income nor a lifetime of inactivity."

Additional details on educational attainment by the elderly within the next thirty-two years were given by Dr. Harold Sheppard, social scientist at W. E. Upjohn Institute for Employment Research. He said that by the turn of the century the number of people in their sixties who will have a college degree will be about nine to ten times more than people in their sixties today. Like Dr. Morris, he thought that the older Americans of the future are not going to accept the retirement pattern of today's elderly people:

"With higher educational achievement... and health consciousness and the effective acceptance of a democratic ideology of equality, I doubt very strongly that the aged in the year 2000 will passively tolerate conditions resulting from the stereotypes and attitudes toward the aged that the young today themselves entertain toward the aged. They will not want to be treated in the year 2000 the way they treat the aged of today."

The National Council on the Aging, which has already begun its own studies of future needs, has been emphatic in requesting an organized far-reaching effort to estimate what the future can and should bring. Milton Shapp, chairman of the Public Policy Committee for the NCOA, in testimony before the Senate Committee on Aging, put the case for systematic projections:

"Heretofore, we have tackled the job piecemeal, and to do so was perhaps wise and even necessary to get a program started. The time has now come for the elderly in certain crucial areas—(1) to measure the need, (2) to define ways of meeting the need, (3) to estimate the cost, and (4) to establish target dates.

"Similar methods have brought results in war efforts, in space exploration, in public highway construction, and—to an extent—in public education. We can do no less with regard to human goals for the older people of the nation.

"Last year, the staff of the National Council on the Aging undertook an assessment of progress in the field of aging since 1950, as background material for our annual meeting, which was on the subject of 'Developing Public Policy.' In many respects, this was a rewarding experience, but it was a sobering one also. We were forced to conclude that, in spite of all our efforts, life in these United States has not changed much in the past 20 years for the great mass of older people.

"It (the NCOA report) did, we believe, point the way to a much more complete study which, taken together with certain minimum standards as national goals, would provide a basis for a national policy for all older people—as distinguished from isolated demonstration programs which at best benefit only a few."

Strong support was given by Mr. Shapp and other witnesses at the hearings for legislation calling for a White House Conference on Aging in 1970. They saw the proposed Conference as a vehicle not only for making the kind of projections requested by Mr. Shapp, but also as an opportunity to re-examine progress made since the last White House Conference in 1961.

The Senate Committee on Aging has gone on record as supporting this proposal. It has suggested that the Conference, together with all preparations for it, serve as the means for developing comprehensive projections of long-range needs that may be expected as the population of older Americans continues to increase.

Hopefully, out of these deliberations, will come sorely needed measures which will make the elderly less vulnerable to the con man and more able to enjoy their harvest years.

Appendixes

Appendix I

Changes In Social Security

The amendment to the Social Security law passed in 1967 was a significant step forward in dealing with some of the problems of the elderly. However, many who could reap benefits under the new provisions do not because of a lack of knowledge of what the law specifies. Here is a summary of the major provisions of that law as prepared for the Special Committee on Aging for the United States Senate. It would be wise for all who qualify for social security or anyone who has relatives in that category to read this material carefully.

THE SOCIAL SECURITY AMENDMENTS OF 1967:
SUMMARY OF MAJOR PROVISIONS

Old-Age, Survivors, Disability and Health Insurance

1. *Benefit increase.*—The 1967 amendments provide for a 13 per cent increase in benefit payments for persons currently receiving benefits. The minimum benefit (payable when benefits start at age 65) is increased from $44 a month to $55. The amount of earnings subject to tax and also used in the computation of benefits is increased from $6,600 to $7,800 in 1968.

The legislation provides for the increased benefit to be first payable for the month of February 1968. It is estimated that 22.9 million people are to receive the increase in benefits and that $3 billion in additional benefits are to be paid in the first 12 months under this provision.

2. *Special benefits for persons age 72.*— The amount of the special payment which is made to persons age 72 and over who are uninsured is increased from $35 to $40 a month for a single person and from $52.50 to $60 a month for a couple. The increased amount is first payable for February 1968. It is estimated that 900,000 people will get new or increased benefits under this provision.

3. *Retirement test.*—There is an increase from $1,500 to $1,680 in the amount of annual earnings a beneficiary under age 72 can receive without having any benefits withheld. Provision is made for an increase from $125 to $140 in the amount of monthly earnings a person can have and still get a benefit for the month. One dollar in benefits will be withheld for each $2 in earnings between $1,680 and $2,880 and $1

in benefits for each $1 in earnings above that amount. The provision is effective for earnings in 1968. It is estimated that about 760,000 people will receive approximately $175 million in additional benefits in 1968.

4. *Benefits for disabled widows and widowers.*—The amendments provide for reduced monthly benefits for certain disabled widows and widowers of deceased workers who are between the ages of 50 and 62. A widow or widower would be considered disabled only if the disability is one that would preclude any gainful activity. Benefits are payable beginning February 1968. It is estimated that about 65,000 people will be made eligible for benefits and about $60 million in benefits will be paid during the first 12 months.

5. *Additional disability insurance provisions.*—The amendments provide for a more detailed definition of disability than is in present law; they liberalize the definition of blindness; they liberalize the insured status provisions for workers who become disabled before the age of 31.

6. *Coverage provisions.*—Clergymen are permitted to elect not to be covered if they are opposed to coverage on the basis of conscience or religious principle; coverage is extended to some employment of a parent in the home of a son or daughter; other provisions affect the coverage of certain state and local employees.

7. *Medicare—Title XVIII.*—In addition to certain administrative and operational changes, the amendments provide for a lifetime reserve of 60 days of hospital care after the 90 days covered in a spell of illness have been exhausted, with a $20-a-day co-insurance provision; payment of full reasonable charges for radiological and pathological services to hospital in-patients; payment for diagnostic X-rays made in a patient's

home or in a nursing home; payment for physical therapy services furnished by physical therapists under the direction of hospitals or other approved agencies. The Secretary of Health, Education, and Welfare is directed to study a proposal which would provide coverage of prescription drugs under Medicare and a proposal to establish, through a formulary committee, quality and cost control standards for drugs provided under various programs of the Social Security Act. The amendments provide for a number of additional miscellaneous changes in the Medicare program.

Public Welfare

1. *Work incentive program for AFDC recipients.*—State welfare agencies are to refer appropriate adult members of families (with certain exceptions) who are receiving aid to families with dependent children to work and training programs operated by the Department of Labor. The Department of Labor, through the U.S. Employment Offices, will meet the employment needs of persons referred to it by three approaches. In the first instance, all those who are immediately employable will be moved into regular employment. Secondly, those who need training will be given suitable training and will then be referred to regular employment. Thirdly, the employment office will make arrangements for special work projects to employ those for whom no jobs can be found in the regular economy or for whom training is not suitable.

The projects must be arranged by the employment office with public agencies or nonprofit private agencies organized for a public service purpose. Persons working in these projects must receive at least the minimum wage if the work they perform is covered under a minimum wage statute. Workers will be guaranteed amounts at least equal to their welfare grants plus 20 per cent of their wages. Day care (under standards established by the Children's Bureau) must be provided to working mothers. The federal government will pay 80 per cent of the cost of training under the program, and the states will pay 20 per cent in cash or in kind.

2. *Earnings exemption.*—The amendments provide for excluding the first $30 of earned income plus one third of the remainder in computing a family's income for purposes of determining payments under the program of aid to families with dependent children. Earned income of child recipients who are full-time students or who are part-time students not working full time are also excluded.

3. *Aid to families with dependent children of unemployed fathers.*—The amendments provide for a federal definition of unemployment for states which have AFDC-UF programs.

4. *Limit on Federal matching for AFDC.*—The amendments provide that for purposes of federal matching the proportion of all children under age 18 who are receiving AFDC payments on the basis of a parent's absence from the home in each state as of January 1, 1968, cannot be exceeded after June 30, 1968.

5. *Emergency assistance.*—Provision is made for Federal matching for up to 30 days of emergency assistance during a 12-month period to a child and his family. This assistance can be extended to migrant families.

6. *Home repairs.*—Federal matching is allowed for repairs (up to $500) to homes of cash assistance recipients if such repair will assure the recipient the continued use of his home and provide housing at less cost than rent for suitable accomodations.

7. *Services for children.*—Child welfare services and services to children receiving AFDC are to be provided by the same organizational unit at the state and local level with certain exceptions for existing arrangements. The authorization for child welfare services is increased from $55 million to $100 million for fiscal year 1969, and from $60 million to $110 million for later years.

8. *"Pass along" provision.*—States have the option of exempting up to $7.50 a month of any type of income for the aged, blind, and the disabled in determining eligibility and the amount of assistance under the cash assistance programs.

9. *Medicaid.*—States are limited in setting income levels for federal matching purposes to 133⅓ per cent of the AFDC payment level. For those states with programs already in effect the percentage is 150 for the period July-December 1968 and 140 for calendar year 1969. This limit does not affect persons who are receiving or are eligible for cash welfare assistance. Other Medicaid amendments relate to the coordination of Medicaid and the supplementary medical insurance program under Medicare, free choice of medical practitioners and facilities for Medicaid recipients, choice of services which the states may provide under Medicaid, provision for deductibles or cost sharing under state programs, and other miscellaneous provisions.

10. *Standards for skilled nursing homes under Medicaid.*— The amendments require the states to place Medicaid recipients only in those licensed nursing homes which meet specified standards. The states are also required to have a professional medical audit program under which periodic medical evaluations will be made of the appropriateness of the care provided to Medicaid patients in nursing homes, mental hospitals, and

other institutions. Effective July 1, 1970, states which provide skilled nursing-home care will also have to provide home health care services to Medicaid recipients.

11. *Federal matching for intermediate care services.*— Provision is made for federal matching for vendor payments in behalf of persons who qualify for old-age assistance, aid to the blind, or aid to the permanently and totally disabled, and who are living in facilities which provide care which is more than that of boardinghouses but less than in a skilled nursing home. The rate of federal sharing is at the same rate as under Medicaid.

12. *Licensing of nursing home administrators under Medicaid.*—States must license administrators of nursing homes in order to qualify for federal matching under Medicaid.

13. *Maternal and child health.*—There is a single authorization for child health programs, increasing from $250 million in 1969 to $350 million in 1973 and thereafter. An earmarking of 6 per cent is made for family planning services. Special project grants are authorized to (a) reduce the incidence of mental retardation and other handicapping conditions caused by complications associated with childbearing, (b) promote the health of children and youth of school and pre-school age, and (c) provide dental care and services to children. Responsibility for these projects will be transferred to the states after July 1972.

14. *Social work manpower.*—The amendments authorize $5 million for 4 years for grants to public or nonprofit private colleges and universities and accredited graduate schools of social work, or associations of such schools, to meet part of the costs of improvement or expansion of social work programs and the training of personnel.

15. *Other public welfare provisions.*—The amendments also have provisions relating to the AFDC program as to the location of absent parents, family planning, foster-home care for dependent children, protective or vendor payments, and others.

Appendix II

List of State Offices Established
For Consumer Protection*

* Those states not listed failed to respond to an inquiry sent out by the Special Committee on Aging, United States Senate, Ninetieth Congress.

Alaska
Attorney General of Alaska
Consumer Protection Division
Pouch "K"
State Capitol
Juneau, Alaska 99801

Arizona
Attorney General of Arizona
Division of Consumer Frauds
State Capitol
Phoenix, Arizona 85007

California
Attorney General of California
Room 500, Wells Fargo Bank Building
Fifth Street & Capitol Mall
Sacramento, California 95814
or
Assistant Attorney General
Anti-trust Section
State Building
San Francisco, California 94102
or
Deputy Attorney General in Charge
Consumer Fraud Section
State Building
Los Angeles, California 90012

Connecticut
Attorney General of Connecticut
30 Trinity Street
Hartford, Connecticut 06103
or
Commissioner, Department of
Consumer Protection
State Office Building
Hartford, Connecticut 06115

Delaware
Attorney General of Delaware
Consumer Protection Division
The Court House
Wilmington, Delaware 19801

Florida
Attorney General of Florida
Consumer Protection Division
State Capitol
Tallahassee, Florida 32304
or
Assistant State Attorney
Commercial Frauds Division
County Courthouse
Tampa, Florida 33602
or
Executive Director
Florida Installment Land Sales Board
2942 West Columbus Drive
P.O. Box 4448
Tampa, Florida 33607

Hawaii
Attorney General of Hawaii
Consumer Protection Division
Honolulu, Hawaii 96813

Illinois
Attorney General of Illinois
Supreme Court Building

Springfield, Illinois 62706
or
Chief, Division of Consumer Fraud
160 North LaSalle Street
Chicago, Illinois 60601
or
Attorney General
Consumer Frauds Division
Supreme Court Building
Springfield, Illinois 62706

Iowa
Attorney General of Iowa
Consumer Protection Division
State Capitol
Des Moines, Iowa 50319

Kansas
Attorney General of Kansas
Consumer Protection Division
State House
Topeka, Kansas 66603

Kentucky
Attorney General of Kentucky
Consumer Protection Division
State Capitol
Frankfort, Kentucky 40601

Maine
Attorney General of Maine

State House
Augusta, Maine 04330

Maryland
Attorney General of Maryland
Consumer Protection Division
1 Charles Center
Baltimore, Maryland 21201

Massachusetts
Attorney General of Massachusetts
State House
Boston, Massachusetts 02133
or
Consumer Council
Executive Department
The Commonwealth of Massachusetts
100 Cambridge Street
Boston, Massachusetts 02202
or
Chief, Consumer Protection Division
Department of the Attorney General
State House
Boston, Massachusetts 02133

Michigan
Attorney General of Michigan
Consumer Protection and Anti-trust Division
The Capitol
Lansing, Michigan 48902

Minnesota
Attorney General of Minnesota
Consumer Protection Division
State Capitol
St. Paul, Minnesota 55101

Missouri
Attorney General of Missouri
Consumer Protection Division
Supreme Court Building
Jefferson City, Missouri 65101

New Jersey
Attorney General of New Jersey
State House Annex
Trenton, New Jersey 08608
or
Assistant Attorney General
Consumer Fraud Division
State House Annex
Trenton, New Jersey 08608
or
Deputy Attorney General
Consumer Fraud Division
Department of Law and Public Safety
1100 Raymond Boulevard
Newark, New Jersey 07102

New Mexico
Attorney General of New Mexico
Consumer Service Division

Supreme Court Building
Santa Fe, New Mexico 87501

New York
Attorney General of New York
State Capitol
Albany, New York 12201
or
Assistant Attorney General
Anti-Monopolies Bureau
State of New York
80 Centre Street
New York, N. Y. 10013
or
Assistant Attorney General in Charge
Consumer Frauds and Protection Bureau
State of New York
80 Centre Street
New York, N. Y. 10013
or
Bureau of Consumer Fraud
State of New York
Department of Law
300 Terminal Building
65 Broad Street
Rochester, New York 14614

North Dakota
Attorney General of North Dakota
Counsel, Consumer Fraud Division
Bismarck, North Dakota 58501

Ohio
Attorney General of Ohio
Chief, Consumer Frauds and Crimes Section
State House Annex
Columbus, Ohio 43215

Oregon
Attorney General of Oregon
Department of Justice
Salem, Oregon 97301
or
Assistant Attorney General
Consumer Protection Division
469 State Office Building
Portland, Oregon 97201

Pennsylvania
Attorney General of Pennsylvania
Harrisburg, Pennsylvania 17120
or
Bureau of Consumer Frauds and Protection
Pennsylvania Department of Justice
Durbin Building
Harrisburg, Pennsylvania 17120
or
Associate Administrator
Bureau of Consumer Frauds and Protection
710 State Office Building
Philadelphia, Pennsylvania 19107
or

Bureau of Consumer Frauds and Protection
1405 State Office Building
Pittsburgh, Pennsylvania 15919

Rhode Island
Attorney General of Rhode Island
Providence County Court House
Providence, Rhode Island 02901
or
Rhode Island Consumers' Council
State House
Providence, Rhode Island 02903

Tennessee
Director, Division of Food and Drugs
Tennessee Department of Agriculture
Ellington Agricultural Center
Box 9039, Melrose Station
Nashville, Tennessee 37204

Washington
Attorney General of Washington
Temple of Justice
Olympia, Washington 98501
or
Assistant Attorney General
Antitrust & Consumer Protection Division
1266 Dexter Horton Building
Seattle, Washington 98104

Wisconsin
Attorney General of Wisconsin
State Capitol
Madison, Wisconsin 53702
or
Assistant Attorney General
State of Wisconsin
State Capitol
Madison, Wisconsin 53702